Homework Helpers Maths

Ages 9–10
Key Stage 2/Year 5

Brian Speed & Linda Terry

We're the Homework Helpers!

We've thought up lots of fun activities for you!

So grab your pens and pencils...

...and let's get started!

An imprint of Pearson Education

Harlow, England · London · New York · Reading, Massachusetts · San Francisco
Toronto · Don Mills, Ontario · Sydney · Tokyo · Singapore · Hong Kong · Seoul
Taipei · Cape Town · Madrid · Mexico City · Amsterdam · Munich · Paris · Milan

Series editors:
Stuart Wall & Geoff Black
With thanks to Fay Turner for additional material and Heather Ancient for editorial development work

These people helped us write the book!

A complete range of **Homework Helpers** is available.

		ENGLISH	MATHS	SCIENCE
Key Stage 1	Ages 5–6 Year 1	✓	✓	Science is not included in the National Tests at Key Stage 1
	Ages 6–7 Year 2	✓	✓	
Key Stage 2	Ages 7–8 Year 3	✓	✓	✓
	Ages 8–9 Year 4	✓	✓	✓
	Ages 9–10 Year 5	✓	✓	✓
	Ages 10–11 Year 6	✓	✓	✓

This tells you about all our other books.

Which ones have you got?

Pearson Education Limited
Edinburgh Gate, Harlow
Essex CM20 2JE, England
and Associated Companies throughout the world

First published 2000

British Library Cataloguing in Publication Data
A catalogue entry for this title is available from the British Library

ISBN 0-582-38150-9

Printed in Great Britain by Henry Ling Ltd, at the Dorset Press, Dorchester, Dorset

Guidance and advice

Schools are now asked to set regular homework. Government guidelines for Year 5 (ages 9–10) suggest 30 minutes of homework a day. Children are also encouraged to do at least 10–20 minutes of reading.

The Numeracy Hour

The daily Numeracy Hour was introduced into schools in September 1999. During this session, teachers focus on five areas: numbers and the number system; calculations; solving problems; measures, shape and space; handling data. The aim of the Numeracy Hour is to develop a child's maths skills, and give them the confidence to solve maths problems without having to ask for help.

All the activities in this book are written to complement the Numeracy Hour. The emphasis is on short, enjoyable exercises designed to stimulate a child's interest in maths. Each activity will take 10–20 minutes, depending on the topic, and the amount of drawing and colouring.

Themes and topics

Throughout the book key words have been set in **bold** text – these highlight the themes and content of the activities, and provide a guide to the topics covered.

Encourage your child

Leave your child to do the activity on their own, but be available to answer any questions. Try using phrases like: That's a good idea! How do you think you could do it? What happens if you do it this way? These will encourage your child to think about how they could answer the question for themselves.

Mental maths

Many of the activities will help children with mental maths, which is a vital part of the curriculum. Encourage your child to try to work out simple calculations in their head before writing anything down.

The activities
start on the next page!
Have you got your pens
and pencils ready?

If your child is struggling ...

Children who need help with reading or writing may need you to work with them. If your child is struggling with the writing, ask them to find the answer and then write it in for them. Remember even if your child gets stuck, be sure to tell them they are doing well.

Check the answers together

When they have done all they can, sit down with them and go through the answers together. Check they have not misunderstood any important part of the activity. If they have, try to show them why they are going wrong. Ask them to explain what they have done, right or wrong, so that you can understand how they are thinking.

You will find answers to the activities at the back of this book. You can remove the last page if you think your child might look at the answers before trying an activity. Sometimes there is no set answer because your child has been asked for their own ideas. Check that your child's answer is appropriate and shows they have understood the question.

Be positive!

If you think your child needs more help with a particular topic try to think of some similar but easier examples. You don't have to stick to the questions in the book – ask your own: Did you like that? Can you think of any more examples? Have a conversation about the activity. Be positive, giving praise for making an effort and understanding the question, not just getting the right answers. Your child should enjoy doing the activities and at the same time discover that learning is fun.

More on Maths

There are many activities you can do outside school that will help develop your child's familiarity with maths and provide valuable practice. Make sure your child has plenty of experience of weighing, measuring, telling the time, handling money, and sharing items out between a group. Look for opportunities to help your child practise addition, subtraction and multiplication. The more practice your child gets the more comfortable with maths they will become.

Numbers from digits

Use the digits below to make some **three-digit numbers**.

The smallest number I can make is 147.

Remember, a digit is a whole number.

1	4	7	9

1 The largest number is ________________

2 The smallest even number is ________________

3 The largest odd number is ________________

4 The number nearest to 700 is ________________

5 The number nearest to 800 is ________________

6 The number nearest to 200 is ________________

7 The number nearest to 300 is ________________

8 The number nearest to 500 is ________________

9 A number that can be divided exactly by three is ________________

10 A number that can be divided by both two and three is ________________

Any number can be divided by three if the sum of its digits can be divided by three.

Favourite books

Robert drew this **pictogram** to show the results of his survey on his friends' favourite type of book.

FAVOURITE BOOKS	
Animal	☺ ☺ ◐
Scary	☺ ☺ ☺ ☺ ◐
Funny	☺ ☺ ☺ ☺ ☺ ☺
Information	☺

1 Fill in the rest of this chart.

FAVOURITE BOOKS	FREQUENCY
Animal Stories	
Scary Stories	
Funny Stories	24
Information books	4

We can see that six faces represents 24 people.

2 Each face represents ________ children.

3 How many children were asked about their favourite type of book? ________

4 What is the difference between the most and the least popular type of book?

____

Sorting shapes

Draw the **shapes** in the correct place on this **Carroll diagram**.

Shape A
has been done
for you!

	has at least one right angle	has no right angles
all equal sides	A	
no equal sides		

A

B

C

D

E

Averages

Remember these words: mode, median and range.

RANGE
is the difference between the highest and the lowest numbers.
MODE
is the item that occurs most often. (It doesn't have to be a number.)
MEDIAN
is the middle number, when the numbers are put in order from lowest to highest.

1 Find the **range** in these sets of data.

(a) 6p 12p 9p 2p 12p ____________________

(b) 12° 5° 8° 8° 3° ____________________

(c) 13p 42p 60p 52p 13p ____________________

(d) 17° 6° 28° 6° 19° ____________________

(e) £24 £16 £24 £48 £27 ____________________

(f) 13° 8° 21° 13° 19° ____________________

2 Look back at these lists. For each list, draw a ring around the numbers which are the **modes**.

3 Now find both the **range** and the **mode** of these sets.

(a) 2 4 5 5 3 4 2 4 3

Range = ____________________ Mode = ____________________

(b) 30 15 25 10 35 5 15

Range = ____________________ Mode = ____________________

4 Work out the **range** and the **median** for each group.

name	**age**
Jack	8
Fred	12
Ella	9
Molly	10
Arlene	7

Range = ________________

Median = ________________

day	**temperature**
Monday	13°C
Tuesday	21°C
Wednesday	17°C
Thursday	14°C
Friday	15°C

Range = ________________

Median = ________________

Remember to put the numbers in order to help you find the median.

5 Work out the **range**, the **mode** and the **median**.

(a) 42p 16p 16p 75p 37p

Range = __________ Mode = __________ Median = __________

(b) 128 143 142 137 143

Range = __________ Mode = __________ Median = __________

Tower sums

Using some of the numbers at the top of the tower, make a **calculation** to match the number on each floor.

Use any **operation** (+, −, × or ÷).

Use each number only once in any calculation.

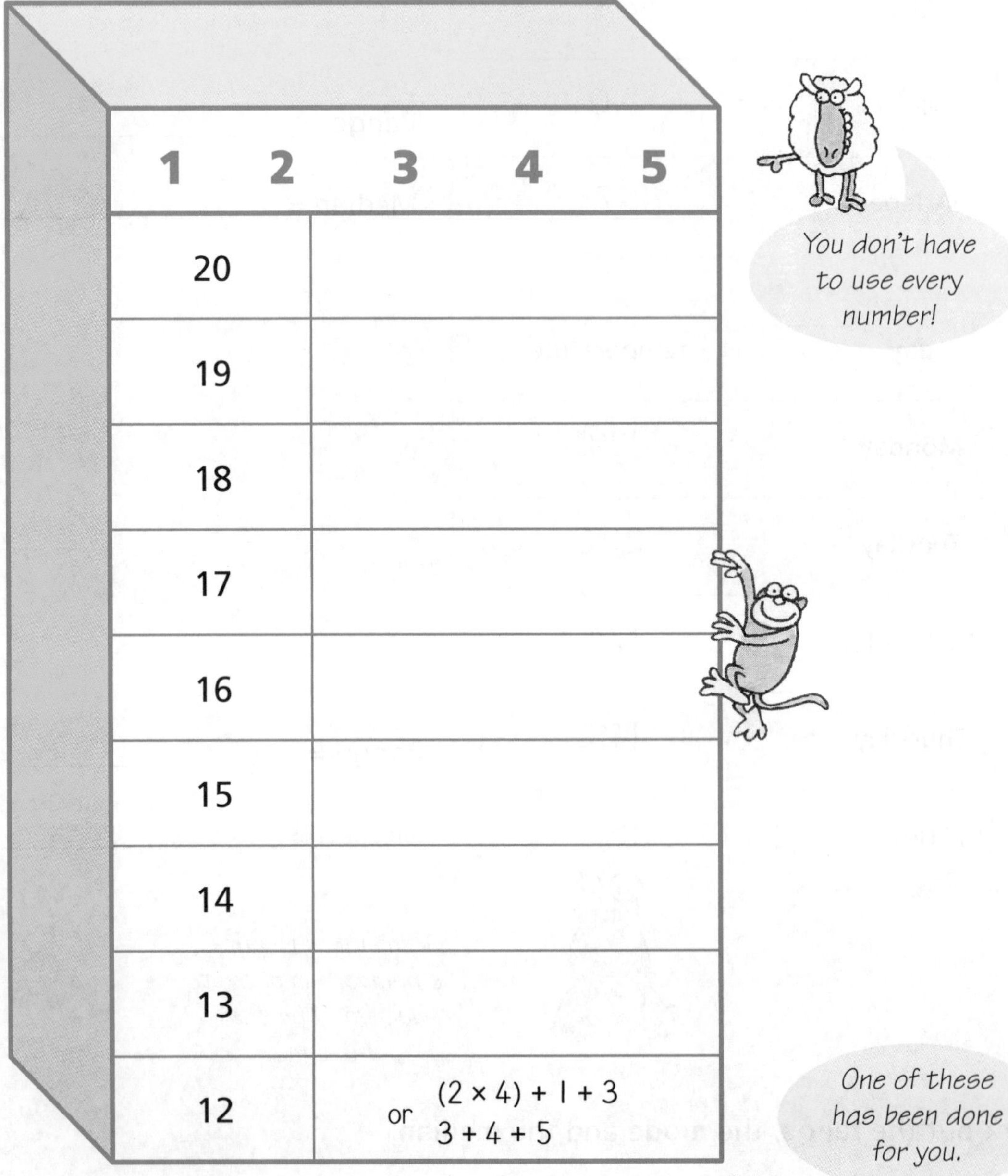

You don't have to use every number!

1 2 3 4 5	
20	
19	
18	
17	
16	
15	
14	
13	
12	$(2 \times 4) + 1 + 3$ or $3 + 4 + 5$

One of these has been done for you.

Now see if you can find a different calculation to match any of these numbers.

Magic answers

1 Choose two numbers from this box.

1	2	3
4		5
6	7 8	9

I have chosen 8 and 3 for this example.

		8	3						
Double one of them.		1	6						
Add 4.		2	0						
Multiply by 5.	1	0	0						
Add the other number.	1	0	3						
Subtract 20.		8	3						

8 and 3 – they were my numbers! Does it always work?

2 Now try this!

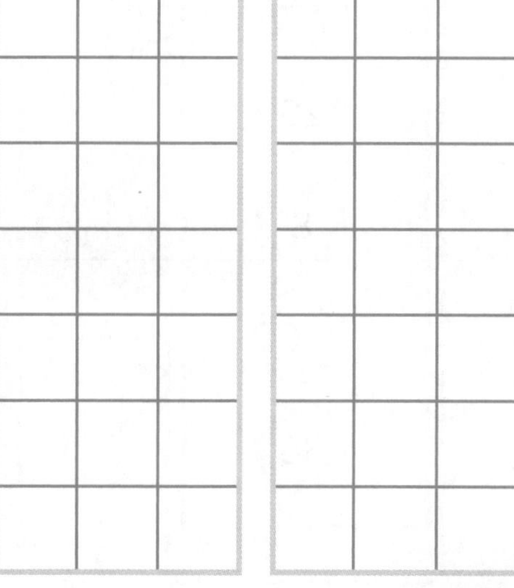

Write a two-digit number.									
Add 25.									
Double it.									
Subtract 10.									
Add your number.									
Subtract 4.									
Divide by 3.									
Subtract your number.									
Add 88.									

The number you finish with is always ____________________.

Number machines

What is the purpose of each machine?

What exactly does it do?

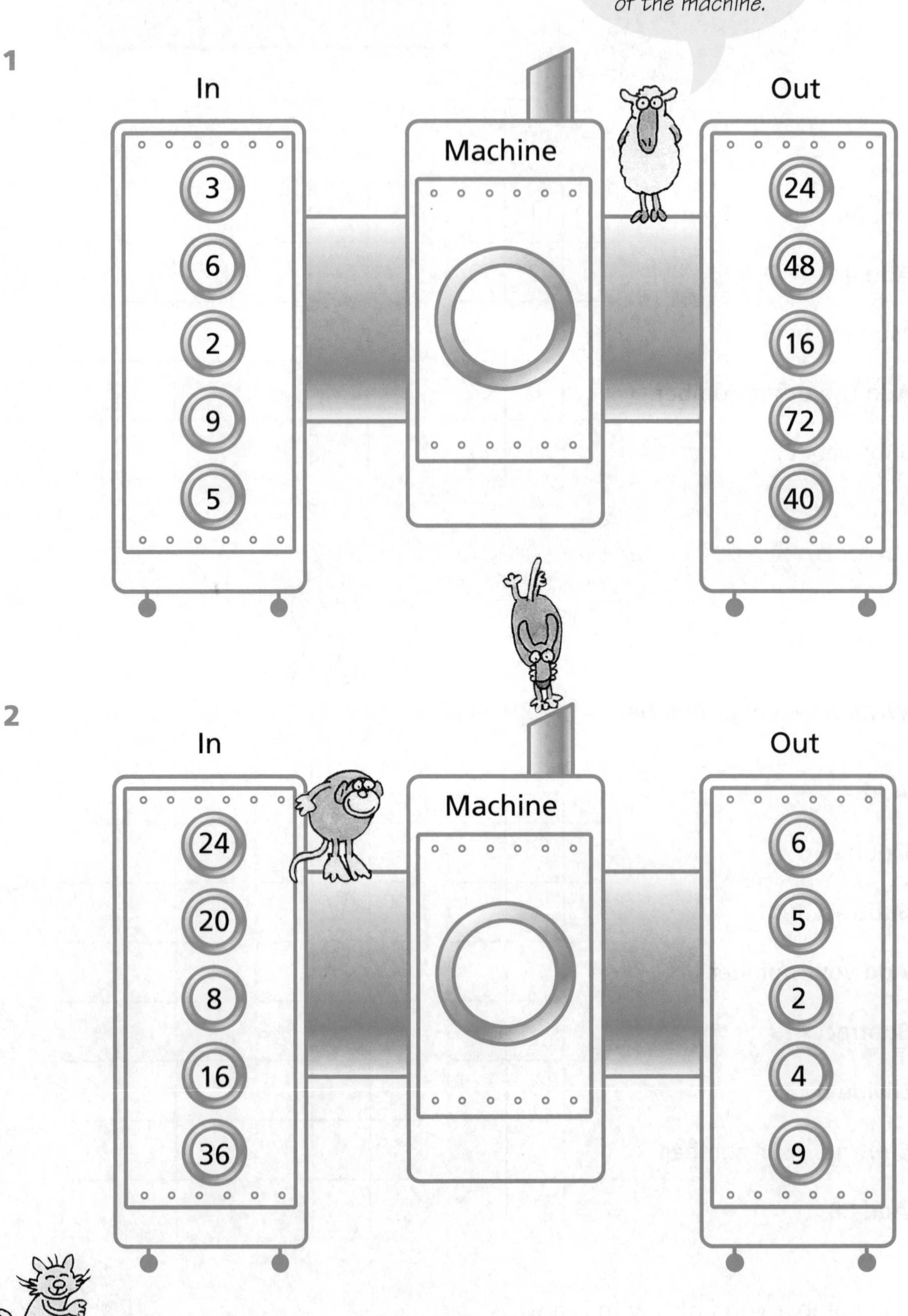

3

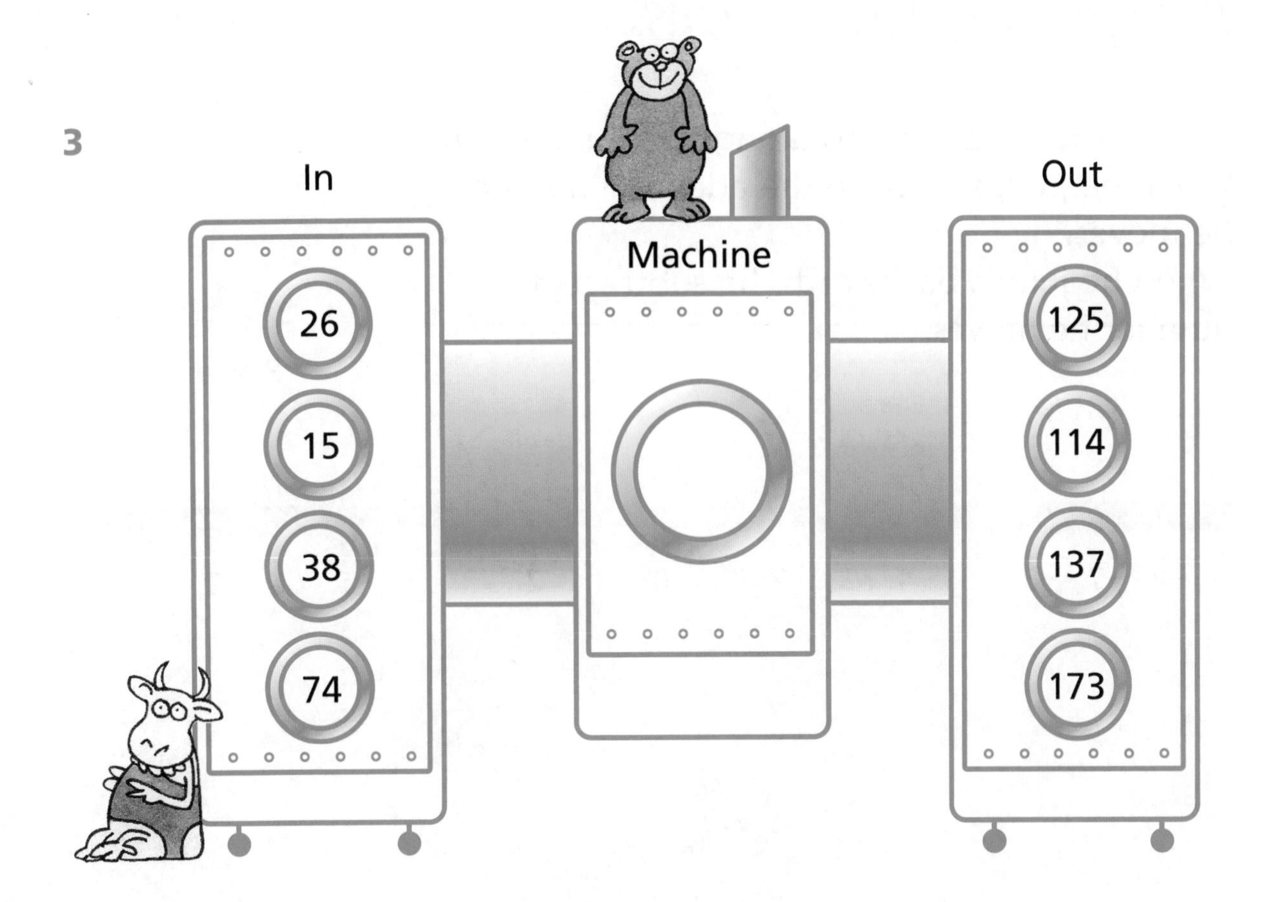

In
Machine
Out
26
15
38
74
125
114
137
173

4

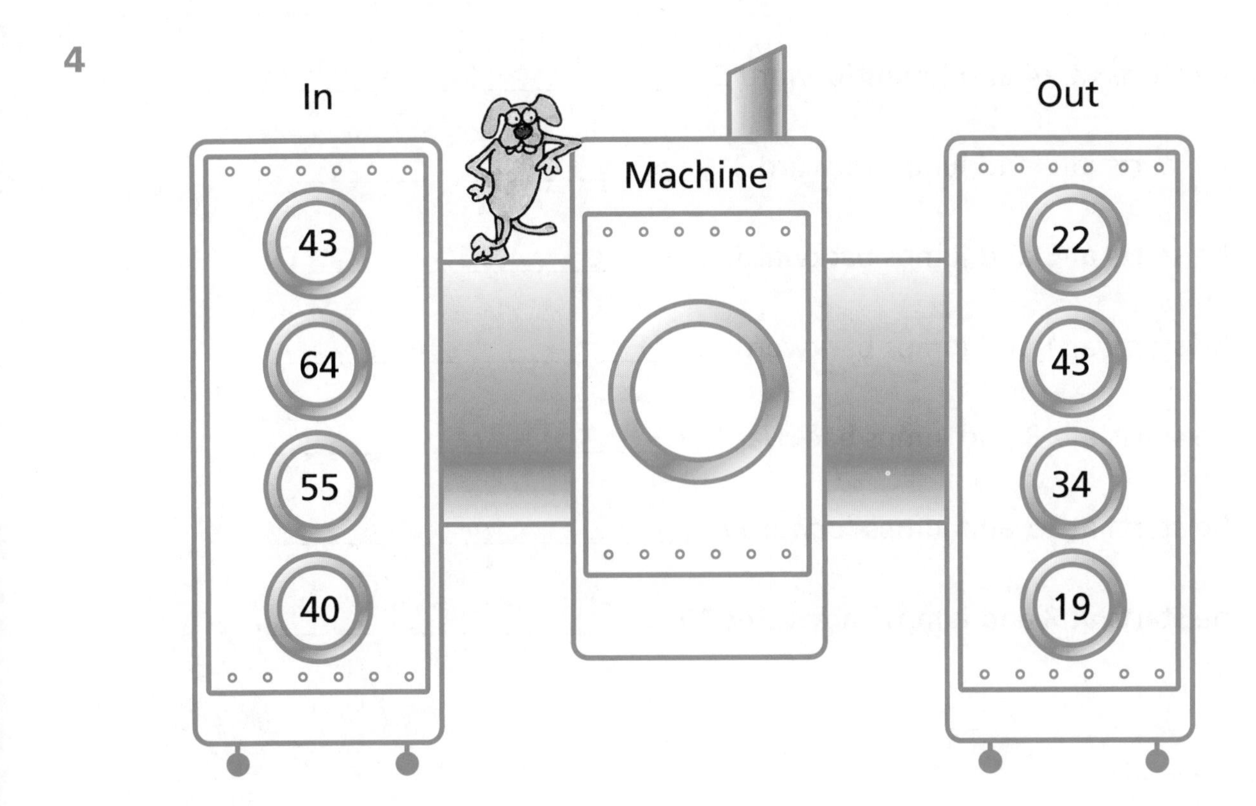

In
Machine
Out
43
64
55
40
22
43
34
19

Negative numbers

Robert the Rabbit jumps along this **number line**.
When he jumps forward, he adds the number he moves.
When he jumps backwards, he subtracts the number he moves.

Robert

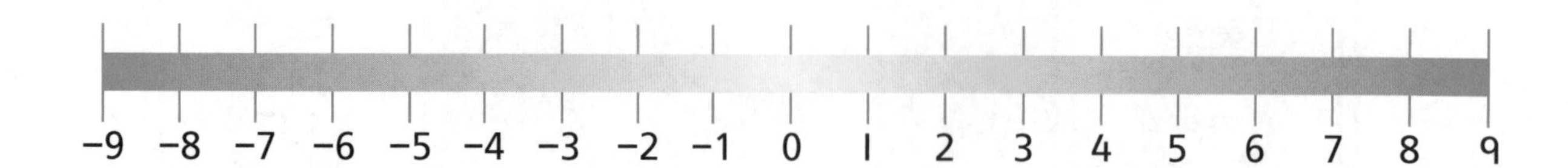

Find where he lands when:

he starts at –4 and jumps forward 3 ______ –1 ______

1 he starts at 2 and jumps forward 3 ____________

2 he starts at 3 and jumps backwards 2 ____________

3 he starts at 1 and jumps backwards 3 ____________

4 he starts at –3 and jumps backwards 3 ____________

5 he starts at –5 and jumps forward 8 ____________

6 he starts at 8 and jumps backwards 10 ____________

Multiply and divide

Use a calculator to do the calculations.

1 23 × 10 = ☐

How do the numbers change? Complete the sentence to explain what happens to the digits.

The digits move ________ place to the ________ and a ________ fills the units space.

2 37 × 100 = ☐

The digits move ________ places to the ________ and ________ fill the ________ and ________ spaces.

3 63 ÷ 10 = ☐

What do you notice about the numbers now? Complete the sentence.

The tens become ________, the units become ________ and there is a ________ between them.

4 125 ÷ 100 = ☐

The hundreds become ________, the tens become ________ and the units become ________.

5 Try doing these calculations without a calculator.

168 × 10 = ☐

57 ÷ 10 = ☐

374 ÷ 100 = ☐

502 × 10 = ☐

89 × 100 = ☐

2575 × 10 = ☐

498 × 100 = ☐

4872 ÷ 10 = ☐

32 ÷ 100 = ☐

Birthdays

Richard asked the children in his class when their birthdays were.

He drew this **tally chart** of his findings.

<table>
<tr><th>MONTH</th><th>TALLY</th><th>TOTAL</th></tr>
<tr><td>January</td><td>|||</td><td></td></tr>
<tr><td>February</td><td>||</td><td></td></tr>
<tr><td>March</td><td>𝍸 |</td><td></td></tr>
<tr><td>April</td><td>||</td><td></td></tr>
<tr><td>May</td><td>𝍸 |</td><td></td></tr>
<tr><td>June</td><td>|</td><td></td></tr>
<tr><td>July</td><td>|||</td><td></td></tr>
<tr><td>August</td><td>|</td><td></td></tr>
<tr><td>September</td><td>|||</td><td></td></tr>
<tr><td>October</td><td></td><td></td></tr>
<tr><td>November</td><td>|</td><td></td></tr>
<tr><td>December</td><td>||</td><td></td></tr>
</table>

Remember, a line through four tally marks means five.

1. Complete the totals in the tally chart.
2. How many birthdays are from January to June? ____________
3. How many birthdays are from July to December? ____________
4. How many children are in the class? ____________
5. How many more children were born in March than November? ____________
6. In which months were only three children born? ____________
7. How many children had their birthday in the autumn term (September to December)? ____________
8. Two girls had birthdays in May.
   How many boys had their birthday in May? ____________

Richard drew a **graph** of his tally chart.

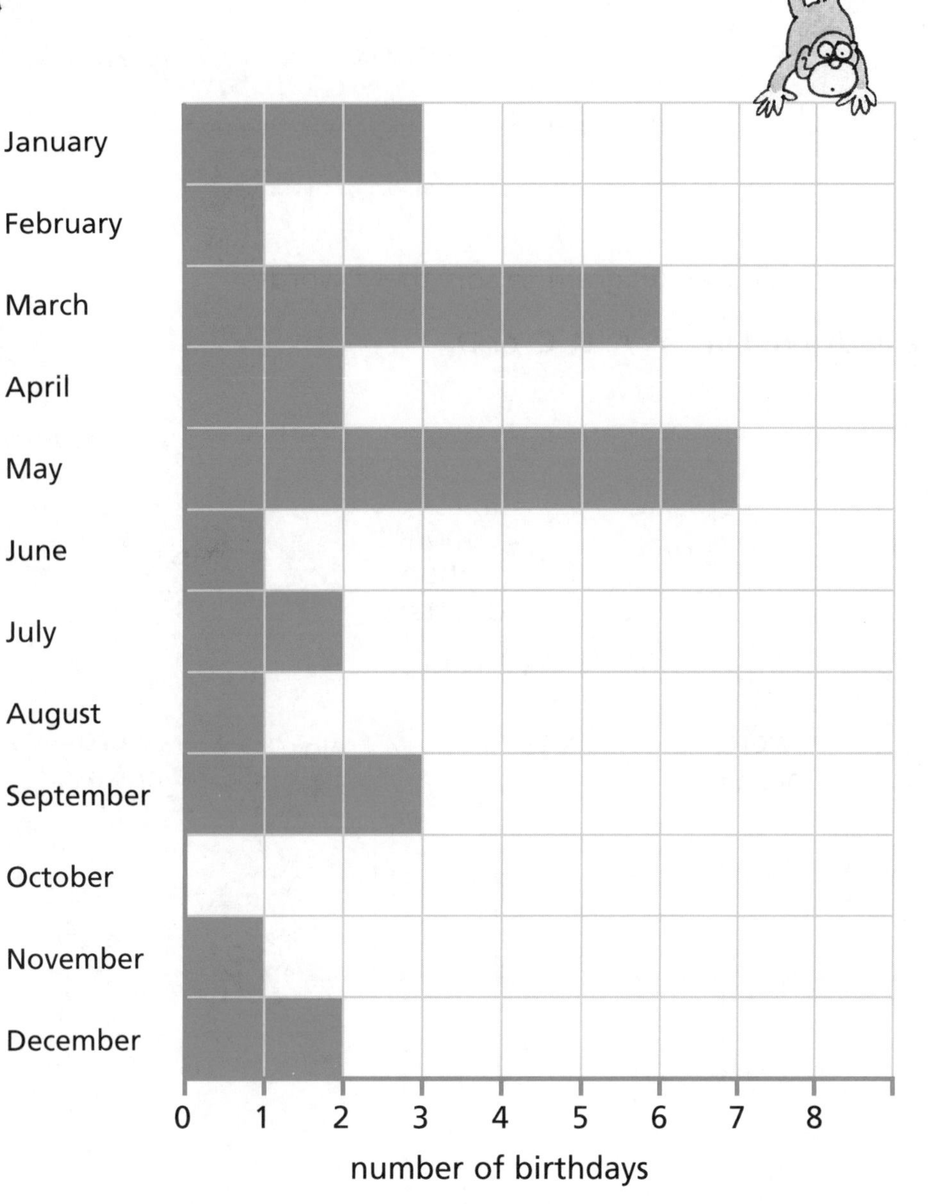

9 Richard made some mistakes. What are they?

____

10 Richard was the only boy to have a birthday in March.

How many girls had a birthday in March? ____________

11 In which month were there no birthdays? ____________

12 What **fraction** of the class had birthdays in March? ____________

13 What **fraction** of the class had birthdays from January to June? ____________

Sorting words

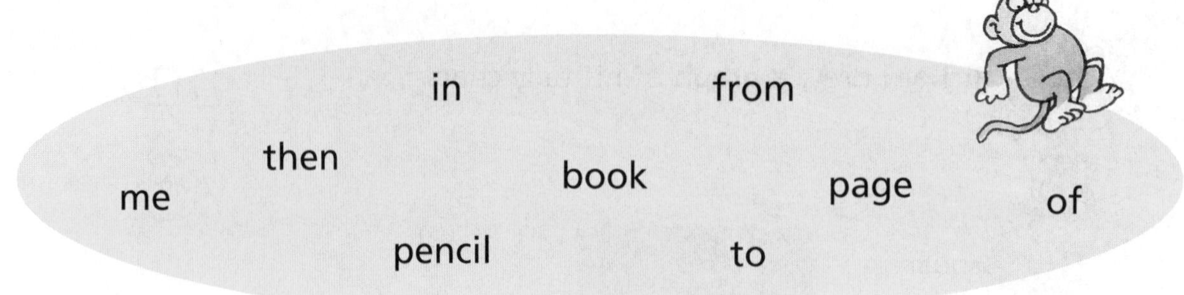

1 Use this **decision tree** diagram to sort these words.

Write each word in box A, B, C or D.

The word 'from' goes in box C because it has more than three letters and it does not contain a letter e.

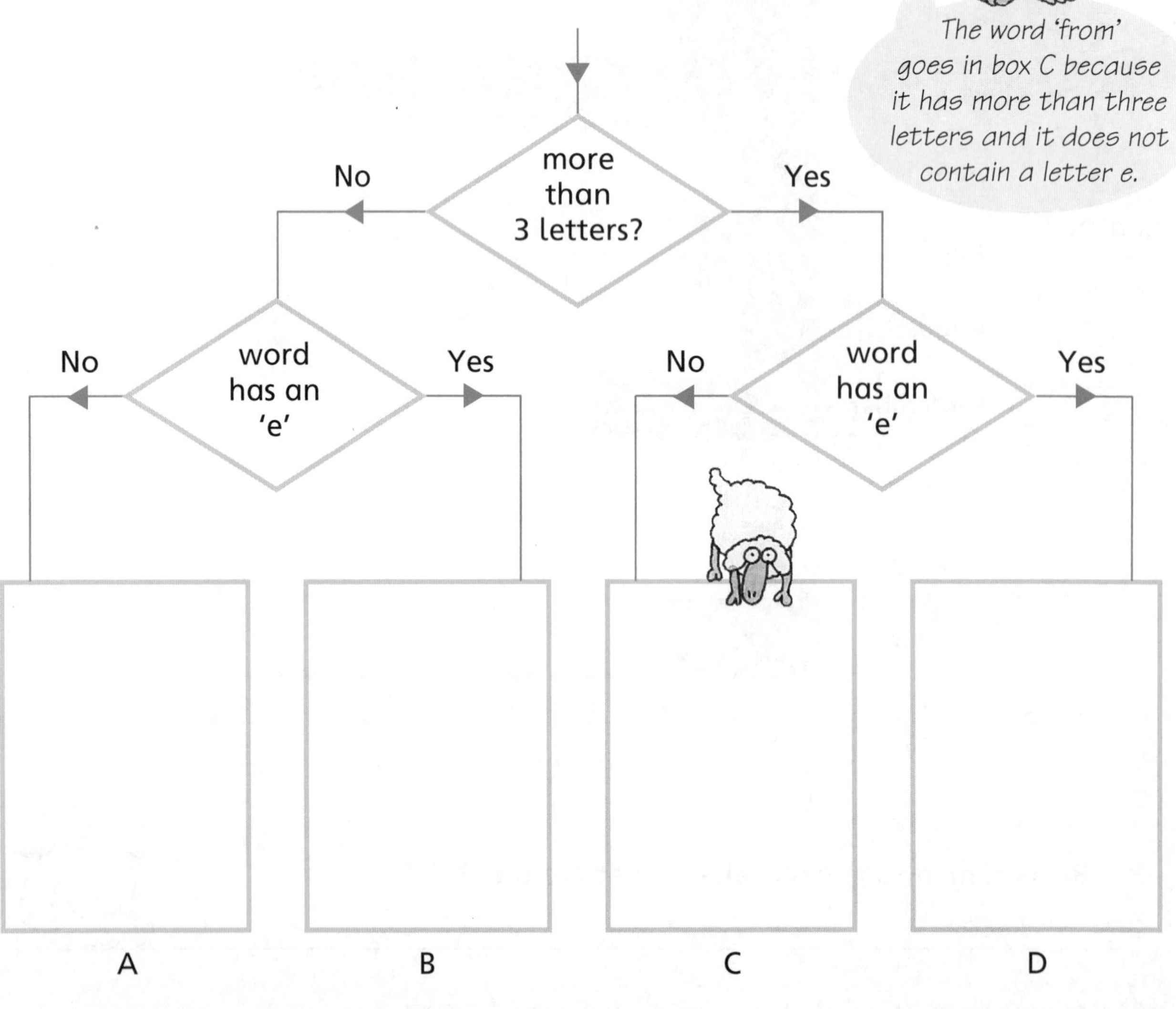

2 Explain the position of 'pencil'. ______________________

____

3 Where would you place 'pen'? ______________________

____

Give two reasons for your choice.

Sorting numbers

Look at these numbers.

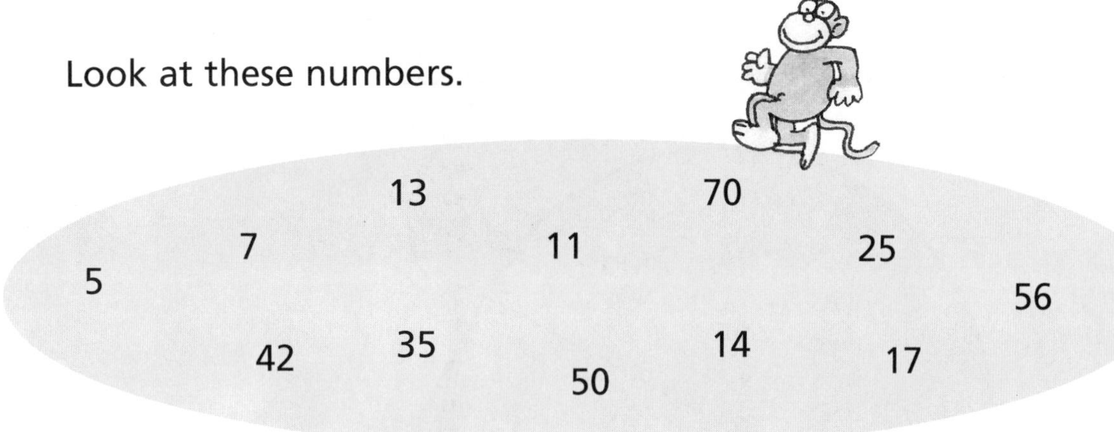

1 Write the numbers in the correct place on this **Venn diagram**.

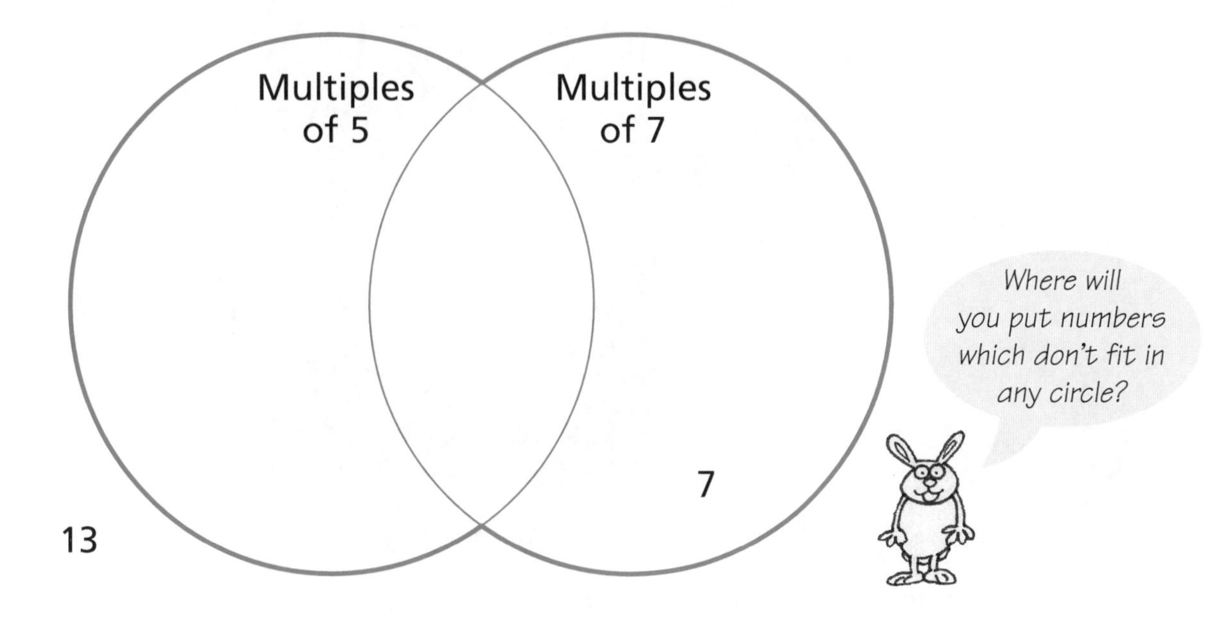

2 Choose some numbers of your own and write them in this diagram.
Make sure you have some numbers in all areas.

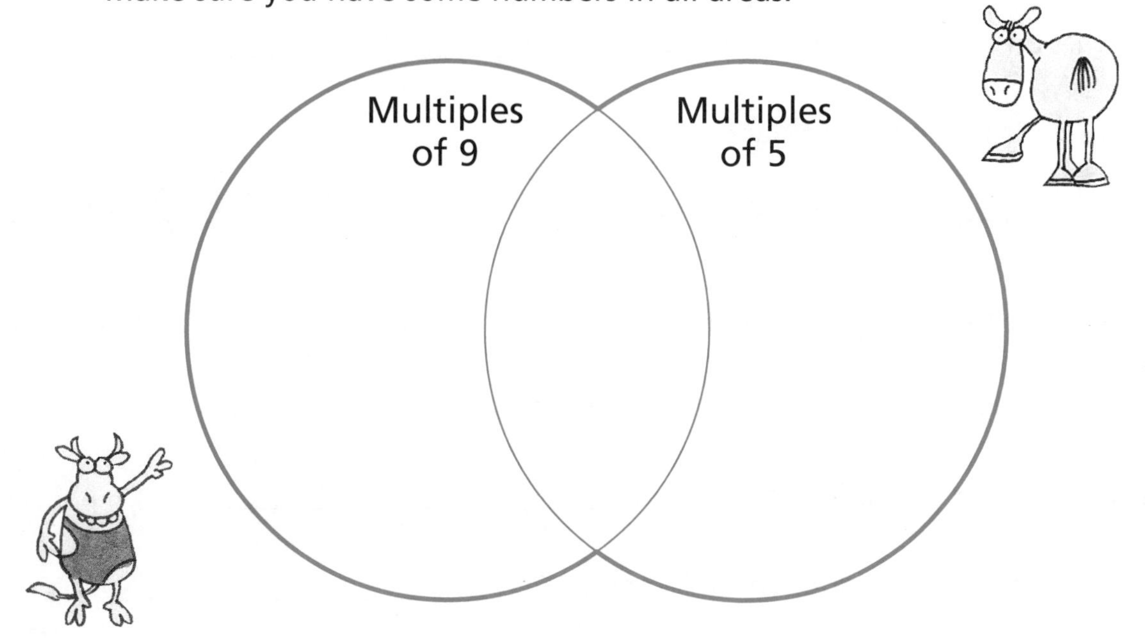

Favourite drinks

This **pie chart** shows the favourite drink of 24 children.

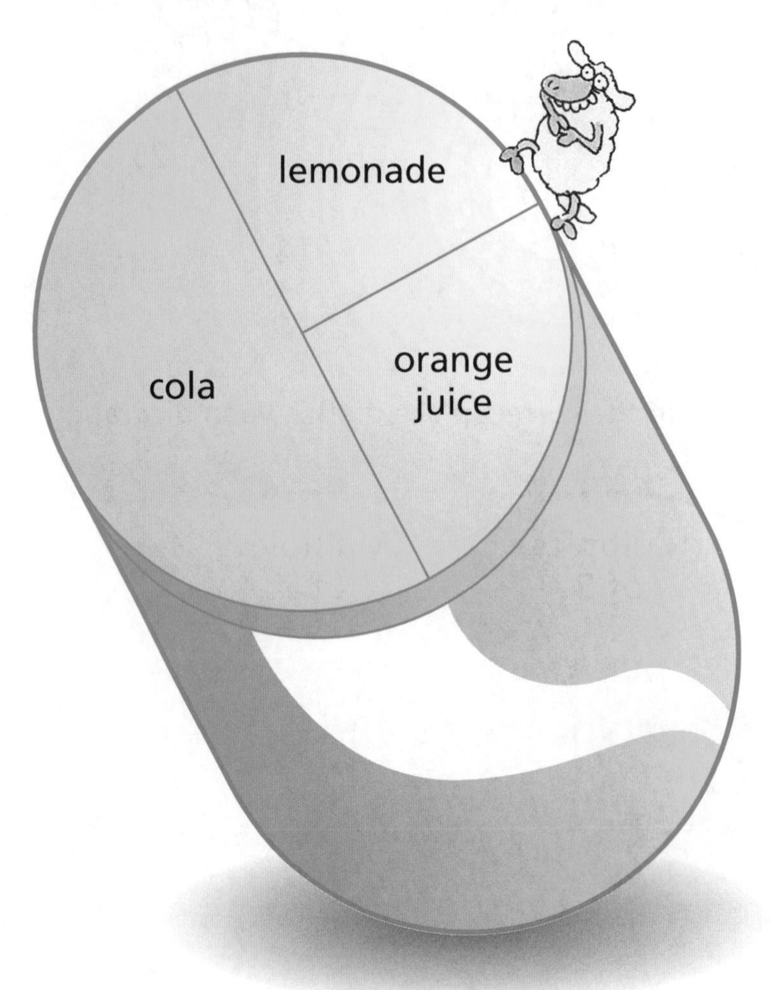

1 What **fraction** of the children chose orange juice? ______________________

2 What **fraction** of the children chose cola? ______________________

3 What **fraction** of the children chose lemonade? ______________________

4 Which drink is the most popular? ______________________

5 How many children chose cola? ______________________

6 How many children chose orange juice? ______________________

7 How many children did not choose lemonade? ______________________

8 What **percentage** of children chose cola? ______________________

9 What **percentage** of children chose lemonade? ______________________

Square numbers

Some of these fish have **square numbers** on them.

Colour them green.

Square numbers are made when a number is multiplied by itself. For instance 3 × 3 = 9, so 9 is a square number.

Flags

1 Colour a flag so that $\frac{1}{3}$ is coloured red, $\frac{1}{6}$ is coloured green and $\frac{1}{2}$ is coloured blue.

Now colour three more flags which keep the same **fractions** for each colour, but which look different.

2 Now colour two more flags which both have these fractions:

$\frac{1}{4}$ red, $\frac{1}{3}$ yellow, $\frac{5}{12}$ blue but which look different.

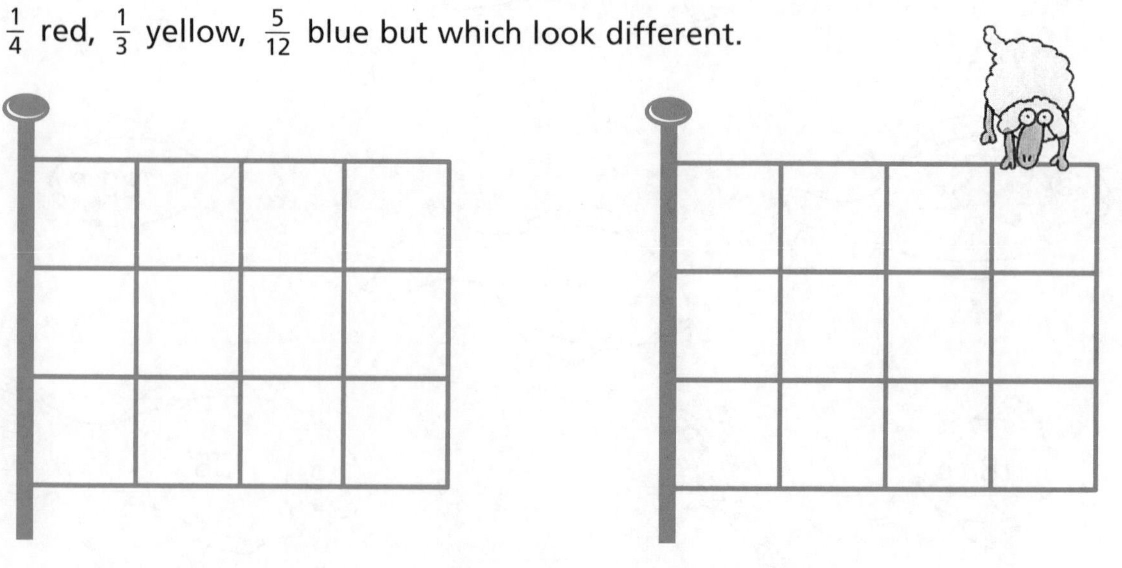

Length

Make your estimate before you measure the line.

If the line is not straight, use a piece of string to help you measure it.

Look carefully at each line.

Estimate how long it is.

A

B

C

D

E

F

Write your estimate in the table.

Line	Estimate	Measurement	Difference
A			
B			
C			
D			
E			
F			

Now **measure** each line accurately.

Work out the difference between your estimate and the accurate measurement.

Abacus numbers

This abacus shows the number two thousand, three hundred and twelve.

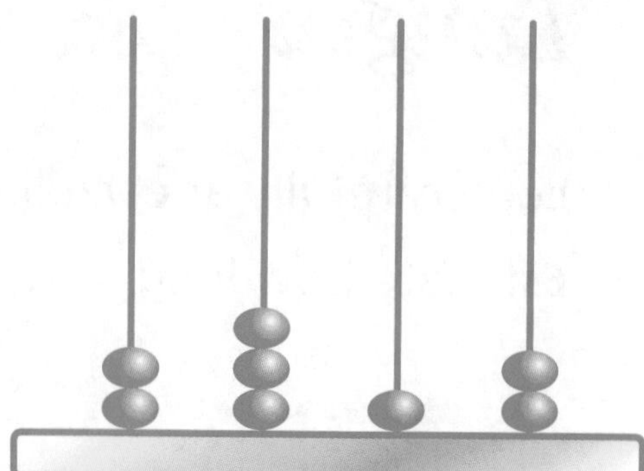

Make each **abacus** match the number.

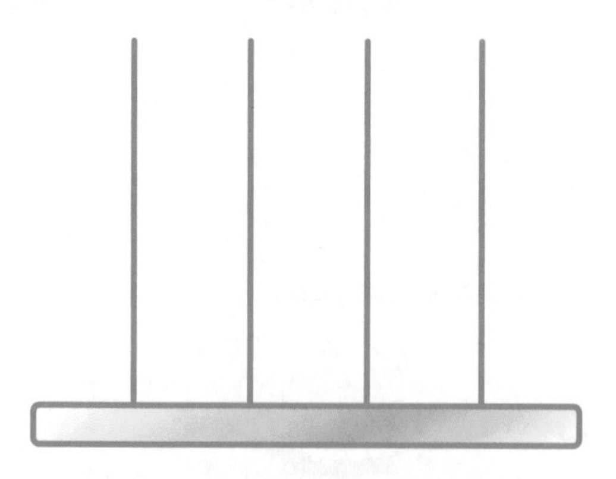

1 Three thousand six hundred and twenty nine.

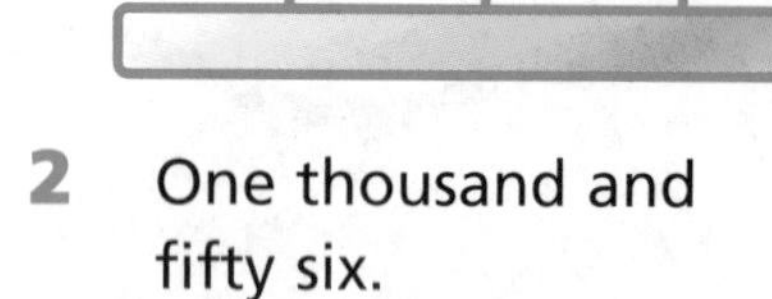

2 One thousand and fifty six.

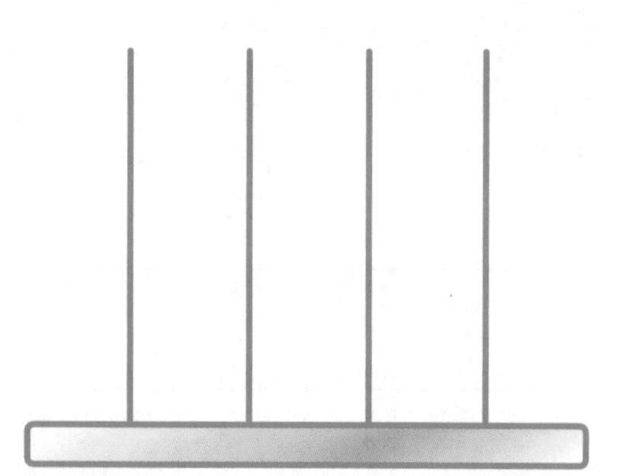

3 Five thousand two hundred and thirty one.

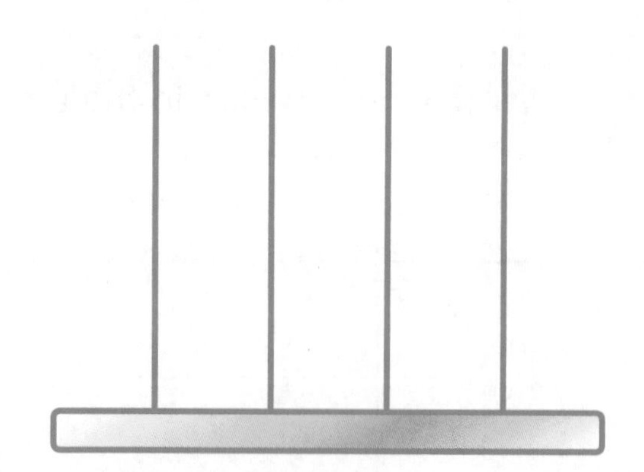

4 Eight thousand and twenty six.

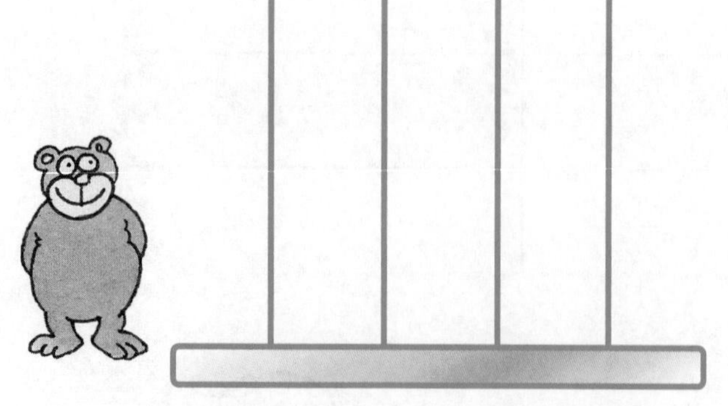

5 Four thousand two hundred and nineteen.

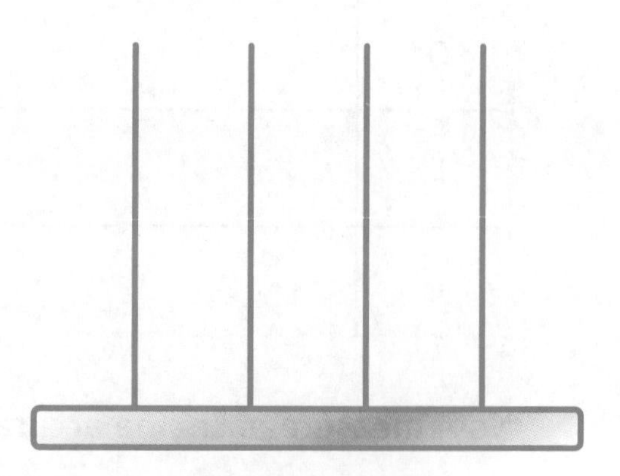

6 Two thousand three hundred and eighty.

For these questions you have to solve the clues before you draw the number.

7 It is an odd number.
There is nothing on the tens rod.
It is a multiple of five.
Two rods have the same number of beads.

Draw seven beads on this abacus.

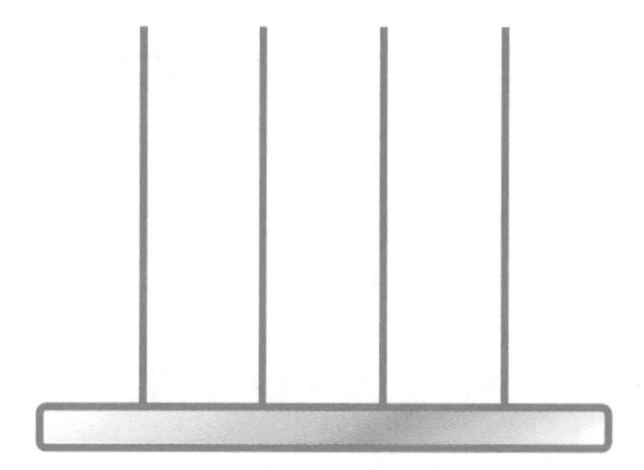

---

8 It is an even number.
It is a square number.
It is a three-digit number.

Draw nine beads.

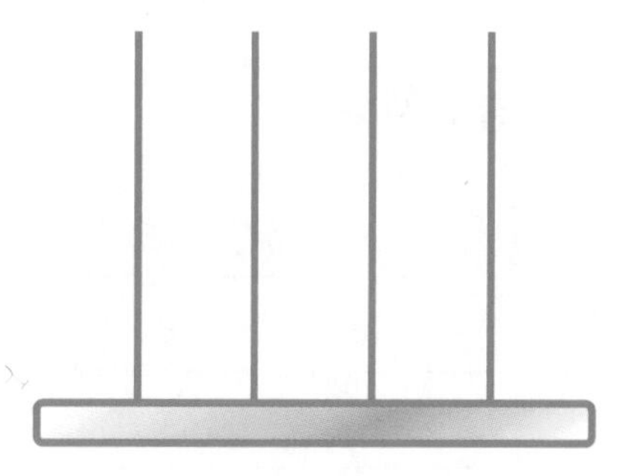

---

9 It is an even number.
It is between one thousand and two thousand.
One rod is empty.
The tens rod has more than the units rod.

Draw six beads.

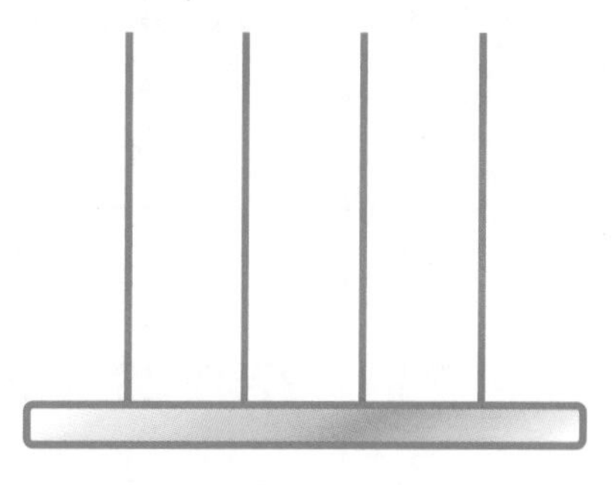

---

10 It is an odd number.
The number reads the same forwards as backwards.
All the rods are used.

Draw six beads.

Times table facts

1 Complete the **multiplication** and **division facts**.

$6 \times 7 = \square$ $8 \times 7 = \square$ $6 \times 8 = \square$

$7 \times \square = 42$ $7 \times \square = 56$ $8 \times \square = 48$

$42 \div 6 = \square$ $56 \div 7 = \square$ $48 \div 6 = \square$

$\square \div 7 = 6$ $\square \div 8 = 7$ $\square \div 6 = 8$

2 Use the pattern from question 1 to write three more calculations that you know for each of these pairs of numbers.

$6 \times 9 = \square$ $7 \times 9 = \square$ $8 \times 9 = \square$

______ ______ ______

______ ______ ______

______ ______ ______

3 On this 100 grid colour all multiples of 6 in yellow, all multiples of 7 in blue, all multiples of 8 in green and all multiples of 9 in red.

1	2	3	4	5	6	7	8	9	10
11	12	13	14	15	16	17	18	19	20
21	22	23	24	25	26	27	28	29	30
31	32	33	34	35	36	37	38	39	40
41	42	43	44	45	46	47	48	49	50
51	52	53	54	55	56	57	58	59	60
61	62	63	64	65	66	67	68	69	70
71	72	73	74	75	76	77	78	79	80
81	82	83	84	85	86	87	88	89	90
91	92	93	94	95	96	97	98	99	100

If a number is a multiple of more than one of these numbers, colour it in stripes.

Test scores

This **bar chart** shows the marks that the children in Class 5 scored in a test.

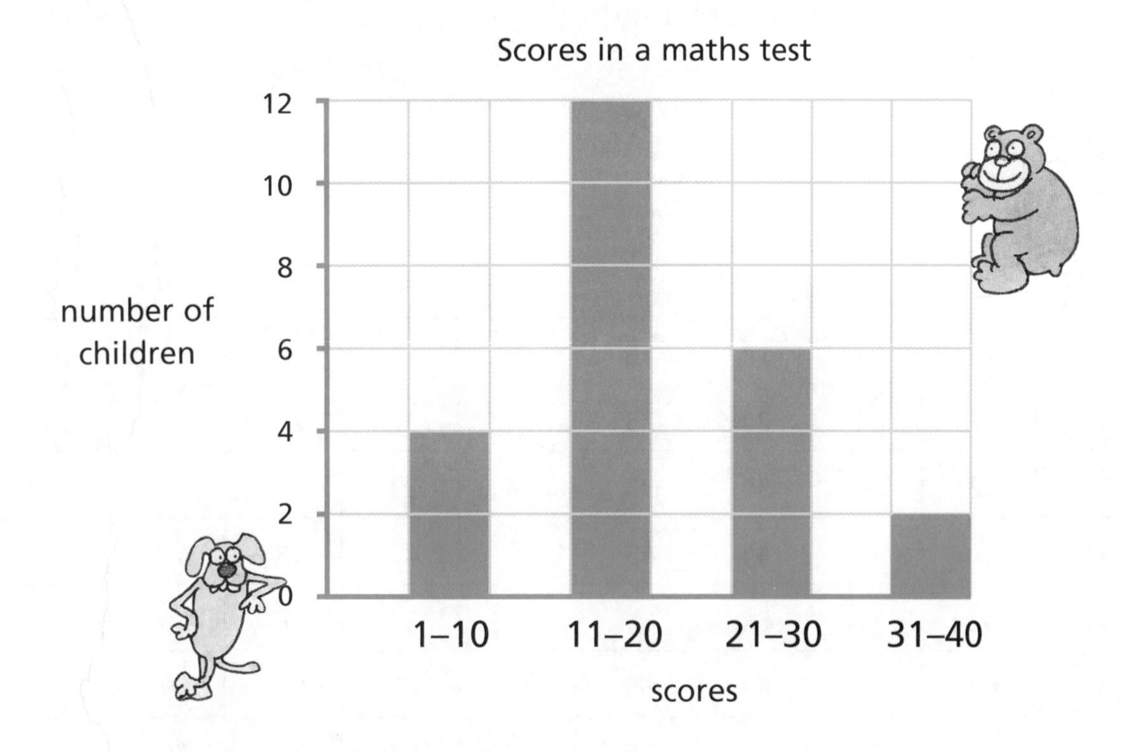

1 How many children scored between 1 and 10? ________________

2 How many children scored between 11 and 20? ________________

3 How many children scored between 21 and 30? ________________

4 How many children scored between 31 and 40? ________________

5 How many people in the class took the test? ________________

6 The test was out of 40 marks.

How many children scored more than 50%? ________________

Here, the ***intervals*** *are 1–10, 11–20, 21–30 and 31–40.*

7 In which interval are there six children? ________________

8 Half of the children who scored between 11 and 20 were girls.

How many boys scored between 11 and 20? ________________

9 One third of the children who scored between 21 and 30 were boys.

How many girls scored between 21 and 30? ________________

Prime numbers

This activity will show you how to find all the prime numbers less than 100. Follow the instructions carefully!

Remember, prime numbers can only be divided exactly by themselves and 1.

1	2	3	4	5	6	7	8	9	10
11	12	13	14	15	16	17	18	19	20
21	22	23	24	25	26	27	28	29	30
31	32	33	34	35	36	37	38	39	40
41	42	43	44	45	46	47	48	49	50
51	52	53	54	55	56	57	58	59	60
61	62	63	64	65	66	67	68	69	70
71	72	73	74	75	76	77	78	79	80
81	82	83	84	85	86	87	88	89	90
91	92	93	94	95	96	97	98	99	100

- Circle number 1.
- Circle number 2. Cross out all the other even numbers.
- Circle number 3. Cross out every third number after 3.
- Circle number 5. Cross out every multiple of 5.
- Circle number 7. Cross out every seventh number after 7.

All the numbers that are not crossed out are prime numbers (the circled numbers are prime numbers too).

1 The prime numbers under 100 are

____

____

____

____

A Greek called Eratosthenes discovered this.

2 A German mathematician, Goldbach, had an idea. He said that "every even number bigger than 4 is the sum of two prime numbers".

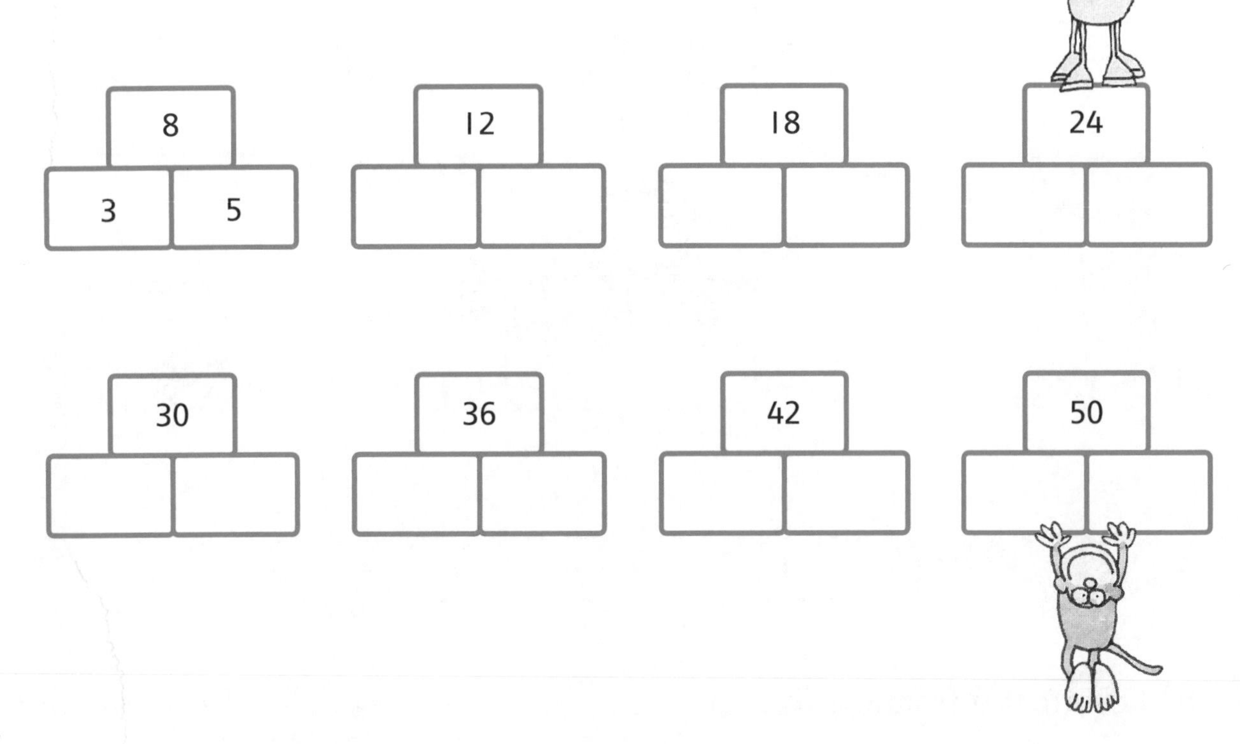

3 Another idea of his was that "every odd number greater than 7 is the sum of three prime numbers".

See if it is true.

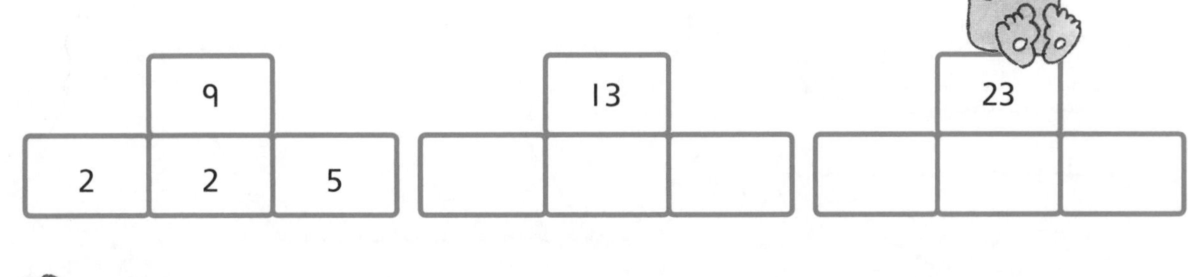

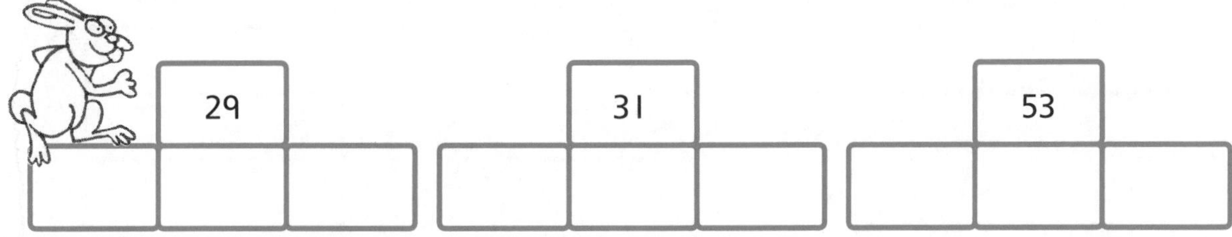

Fractions

What **fraction** of each shape has been shaded? Write the fraction in the box.

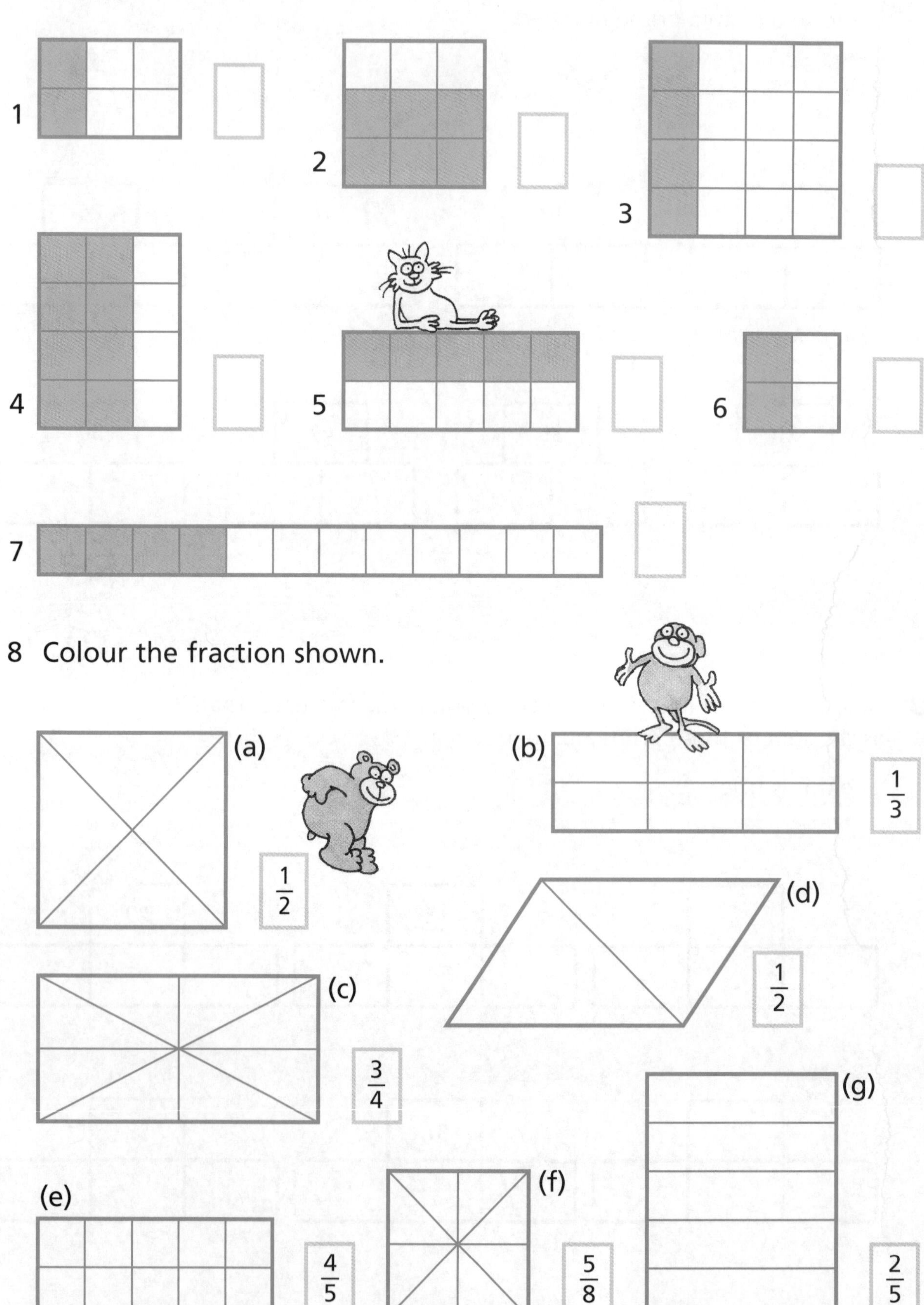

Target practice

Target 8

Roll two dice.
Add the numbers to find the total.
Multiply the total by eight.

+ × 8 = 24

If the answer is on the grid then cover it with a counter.

*This will help you practise your **eight times table**.*
You can time how long it takes you to cover all the squares. See if you can do it quicker on your next go!
You can play this game more than once.

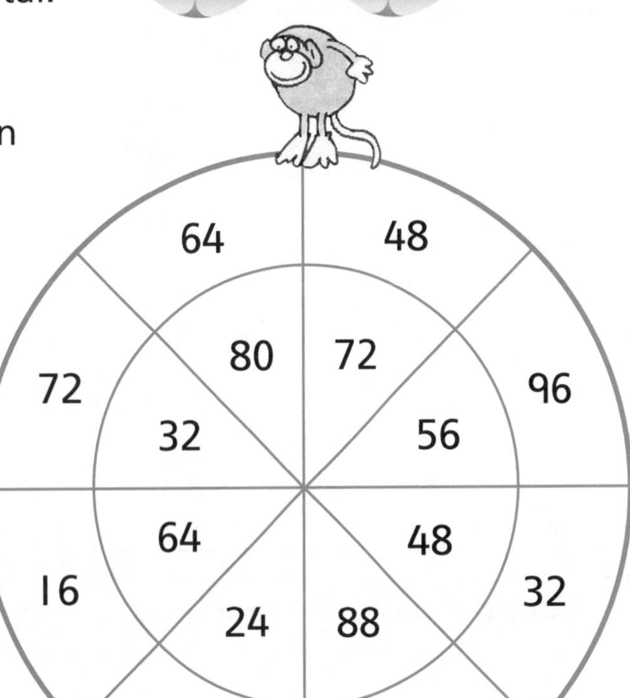

Target 6

Now try Target six.

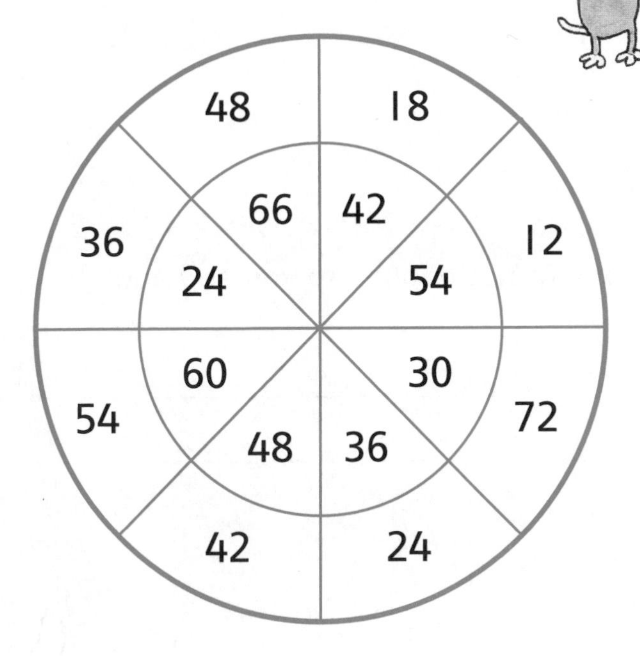

Target 7

Now try Target seven.

49
63
14
28
42
28
70
21
84
49
35
56
56
63
42
77

Probability

1 Write the letter of each of these events on the probability line to show its chance of happening.
(The first has been done for you.)

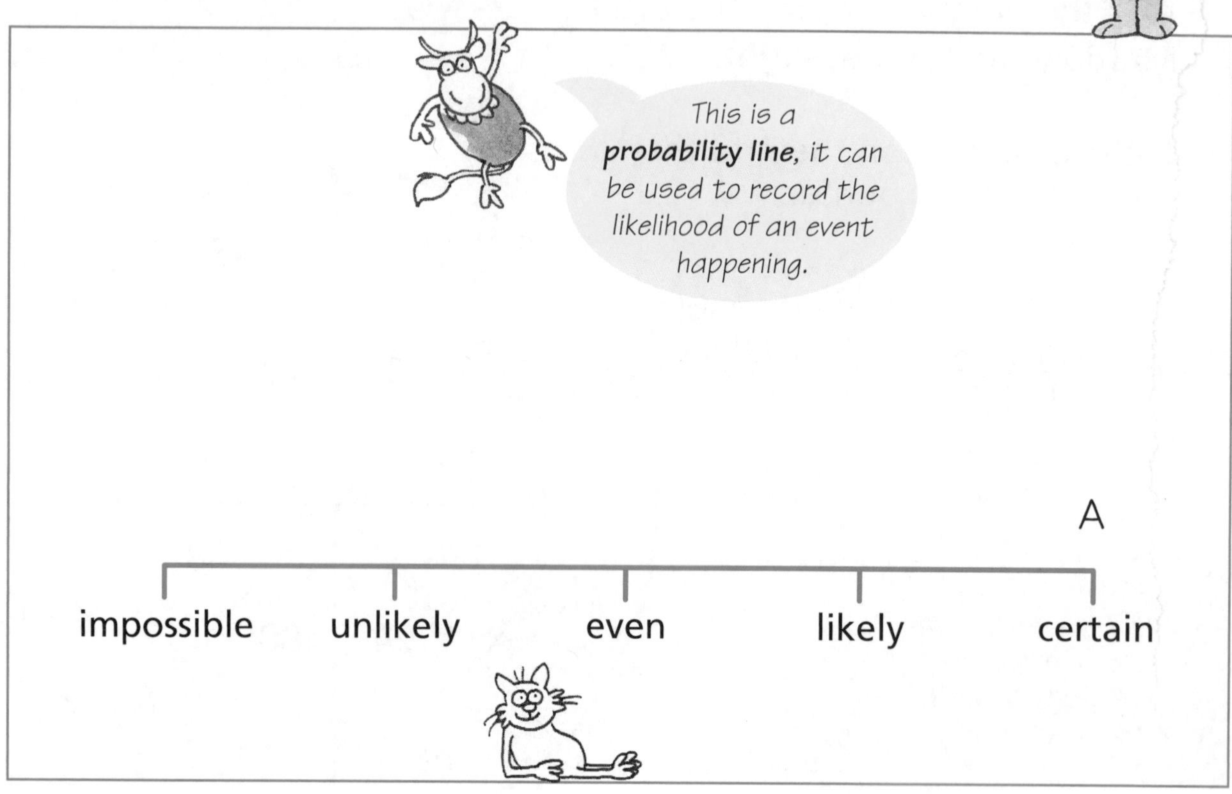

This is a **probability line**, it can be used to record the likelihood of an event happening.
A
impossible
unlikely
even
likely
certain

A Next year, Christmas Day will be on 25 December.

B Next year will be 1798.

C You will get a 'tail' when you toss a coin.

D A pink elephant will fly past you today.

E You will watch TV this week.

F It will rain all day tomorrow.

G You will eat tomorrow.

Think of two more things that might or might not happen to you and add them to the probability line.

H ______________________________

I ______________________________

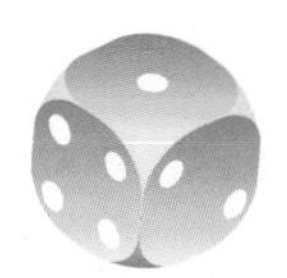

2 Use a dice.
Roll it 20 times.
If the number is even, colour a square red.
If the number is odd, colour a square blue.

If you did this activity again, would your answer be the same?
Explain your answer.

____

____

3 Lucy and Jill are playing a game using spinners.

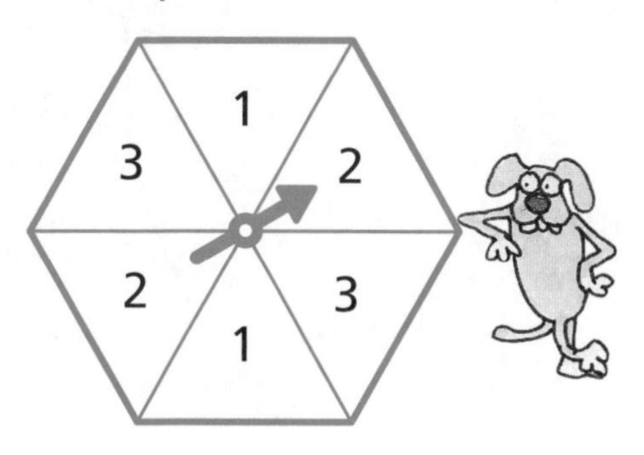

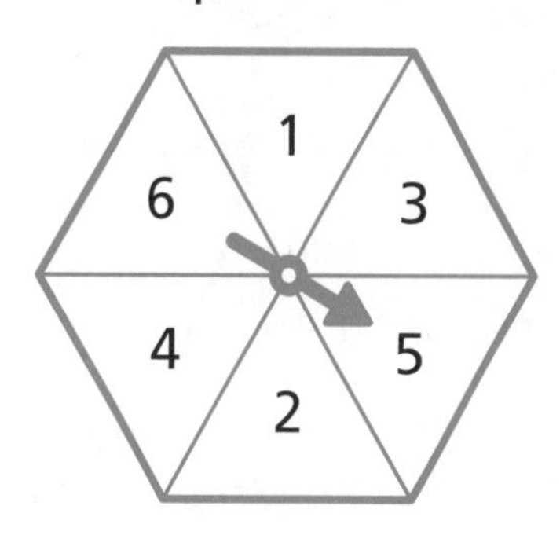

Jill needs a two to win the game.
Which spinner should she choose? ________________

Why? ____

____

4 Lucy needs at least a three to win.
Which spinner should she choose? ________________

Why? ____

____

Who plays what?

This **Venn diagram** shows which children in class 5H go swimming, play football or play netball.

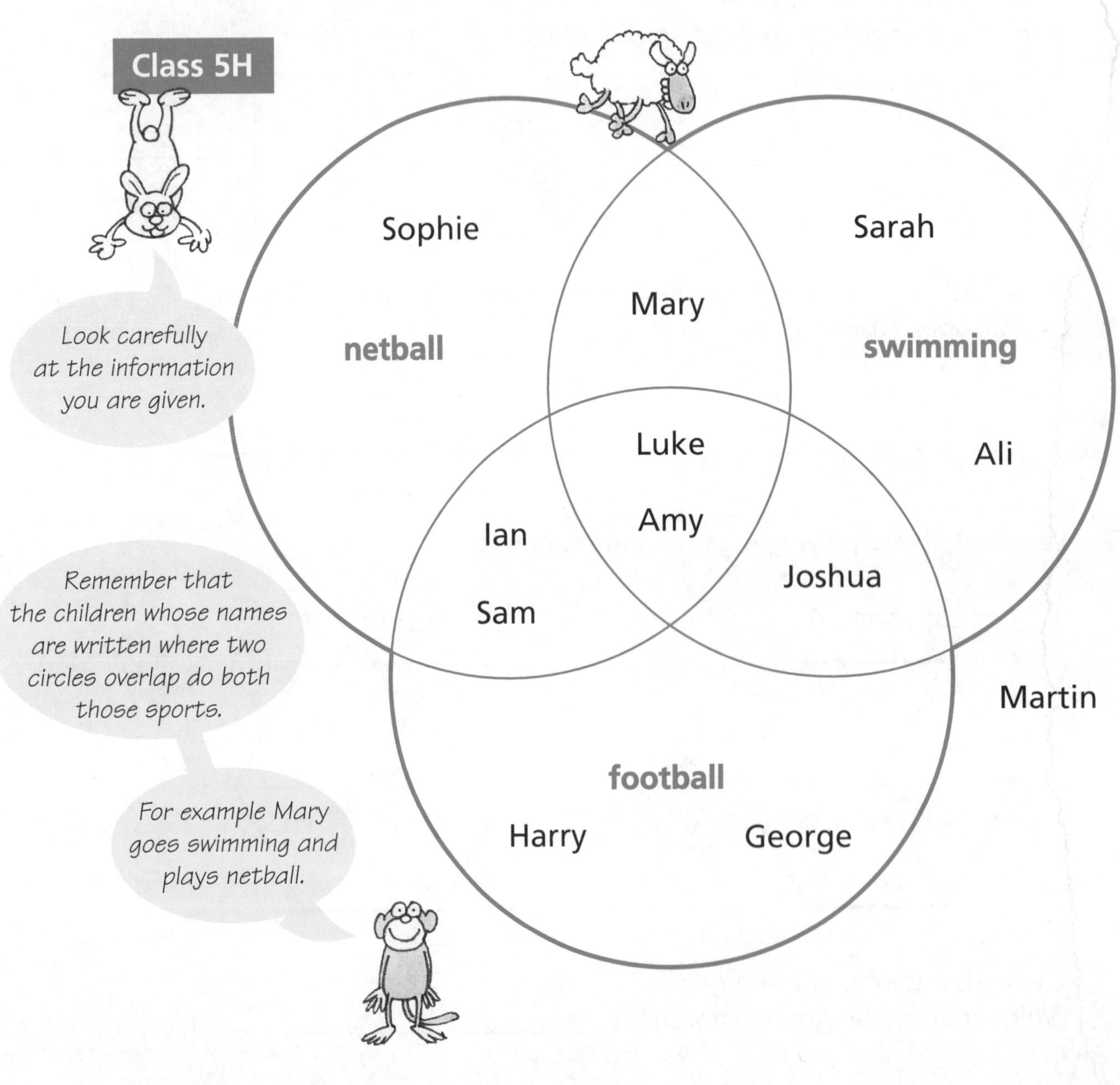
Class 5H
Look carefully at the information you are given.
Remember that the children whose names are written where two circles overlap do both those sports.
For example Mary goes swimming and plays netball.
netball
swimming
football
Sophie
Sarah
Mary
Luke
Amy
Ali
Ian
Sam
Joshua
Martin
Harry
George

1 How many children were asked which sport they took part in? ______________

2 Which sport did Sophie play? ______________

3 What sports did Joshua play? ______________

4 Who took part in none of the sports? ______________

5 How many children went swimming? ______________

6 How many children only played football? ______________

7 Write a sentence about Ian's choice.

____

8 Who took part in all three sports? ____________________

9 Use this information to complete the diagram about class 5P:

Swimming: Paul, Sean, Hannah, Alice, Shasta, Ellie

Football: John, Josie, Lauren, Sean, Paul, Michael, Alice

Netball: Isabel, Rosie, Alice, Josie, Luke, Andy, Hannah

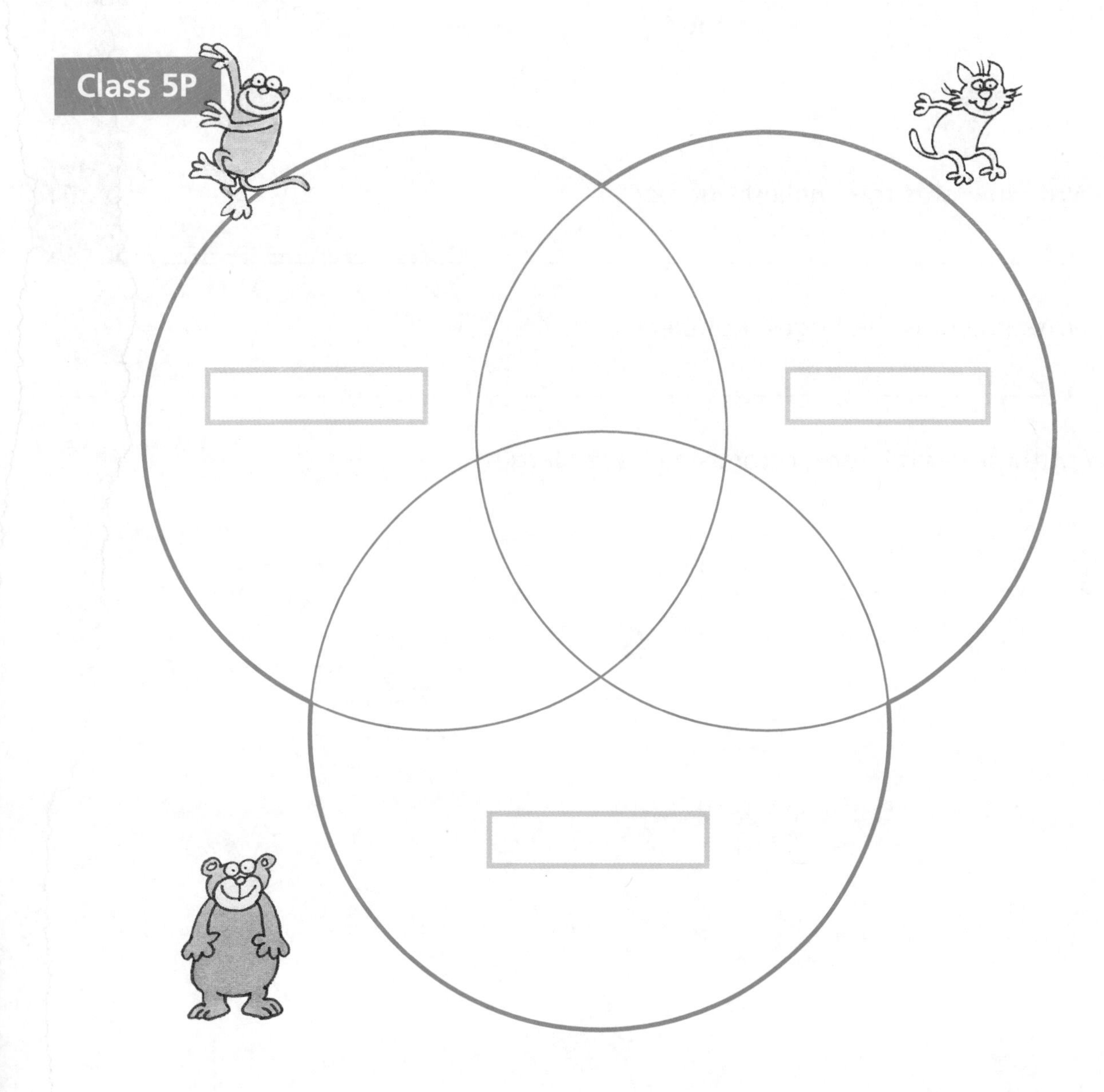

Number order

1 Put these numbers on the shirts in the **right order** starting with the smallest on the left. Two of the shirts already have numbers.

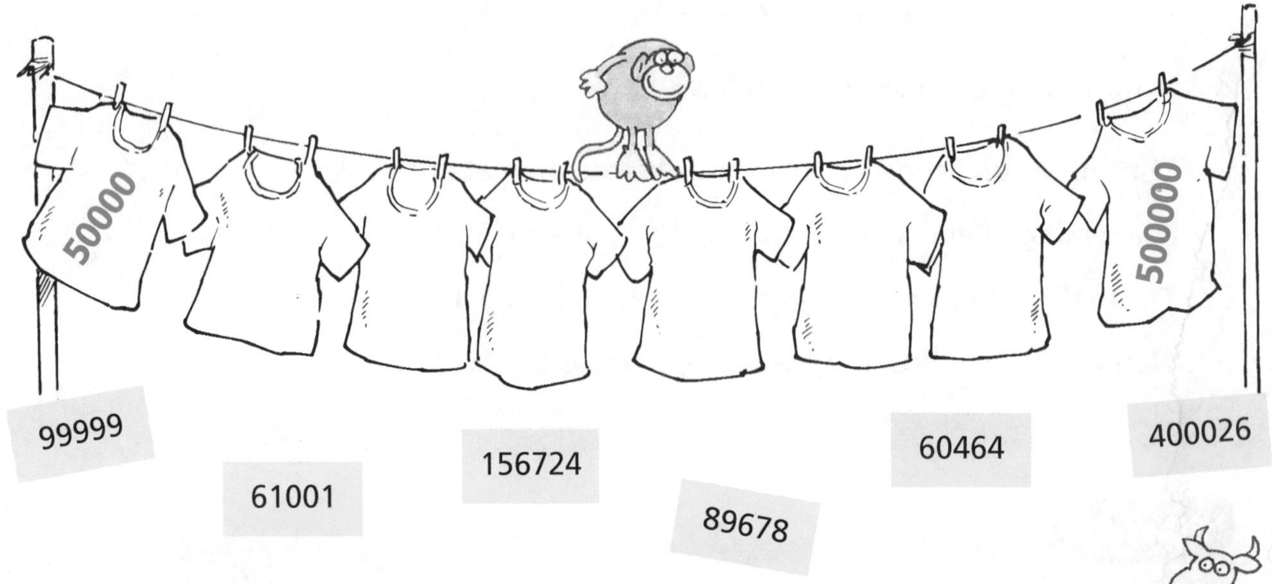

2 Write in words the smallest number.

____

3 Write in words the largest number.

____

4 Put these cards in order from smallest to largest.

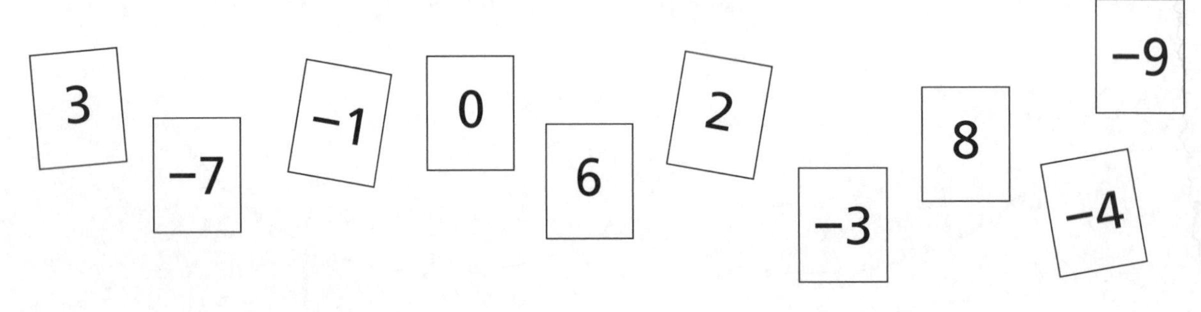

Adding in columns

To **add** numbers with three digits or more, split them up into hundreds, tens and units to make it easier, like this:

396 + 458 →	300 + 400	= 700
	90 + 50	= 140
	6 + 8	= +14
		854

or like this:

$$\begin{array}{r} 396 \\ +458 \\ \hline 854 \\ \hline {}_{1\,1} \end{array}$$

Here you add the units first and carry the tens over. Then add the tens and carry the hundreds over. Lastly add the hundreds.

You should get the same answer whichever way you use.

Try these using both ways.

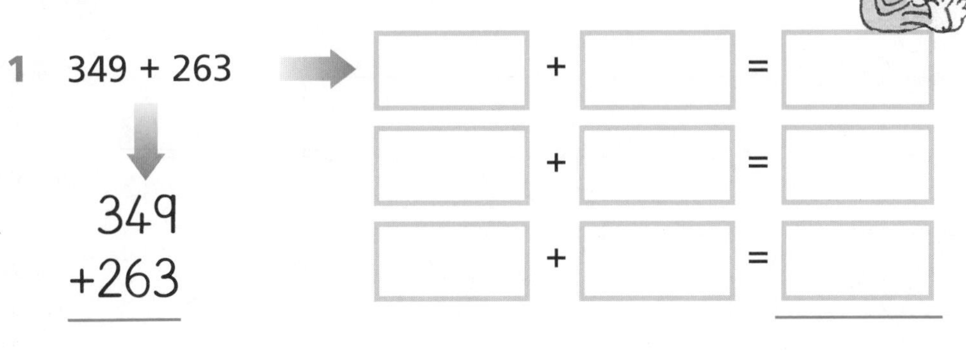

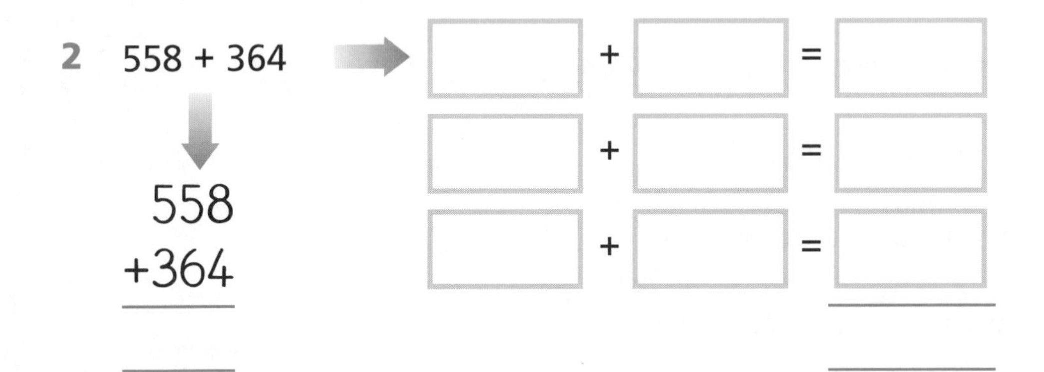

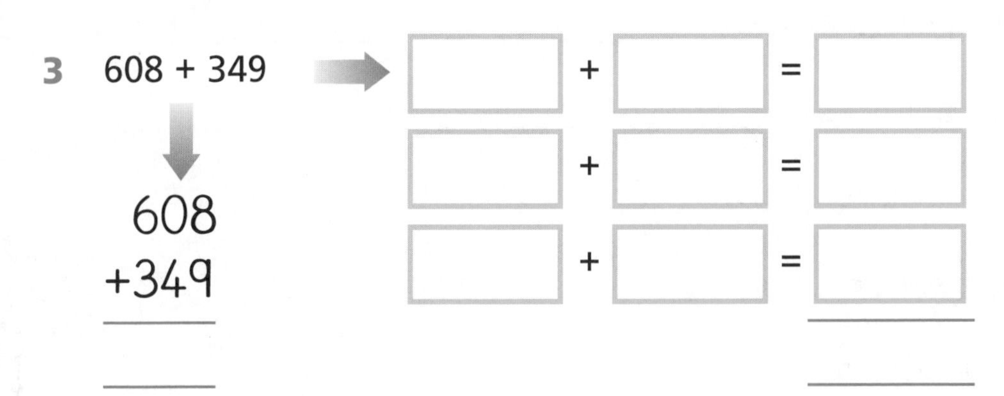

Test scores

Mrs Hendry's class had a tables test.
There were 25 questions.
24 children took part in the test.

Here are their scores.

17	16	21	16	18	17	18	10
14	4	14	6	2	8	25	12
9	19	13	17	21	17	15	12

1 Use this information to complete the **tally chart**.
Notice the data is grouped in intervals.

INTERVAL	TALLY	TOTAL
1–5		
6–10		
11–15		
16–20		
21–25		

2 How many marks are there in each interval? ________________

3 How many children scored ten or less? ________________

4 How many children scored 21 or more? ________________

5 Which interval were most children in? ________________

6 Only two children scored between __________ and __________

7 How many children scored 18? ________________

8 In which interval are they? ________________

9 18 children had a score of ________________ or more.

10 What is the range of scores? ________________

Remember, the range is the difference between the highest and lowest number.

Stepping stones

Polly wants to go home. Can you help her?

She can only walk on stones which have **prime numbers** as answers to the calculations on them.

Colour the stones she can walk on.

Decimals

1 Put these numbers on the shorts in the right order, smallest on the left, largest on the right.

0·21 1·23 1·08 0·72 0·09 0·13

2 Which number is at each of the letters a–f? For each one write the nearest whole number as well.

	number	nearest whole number
(a)	0·8	1
(b)		
(c)		
(d)		
(e)		
(f)		

The first one is done for you.

3 Draw lines to join pairs of **decimals** which make one.

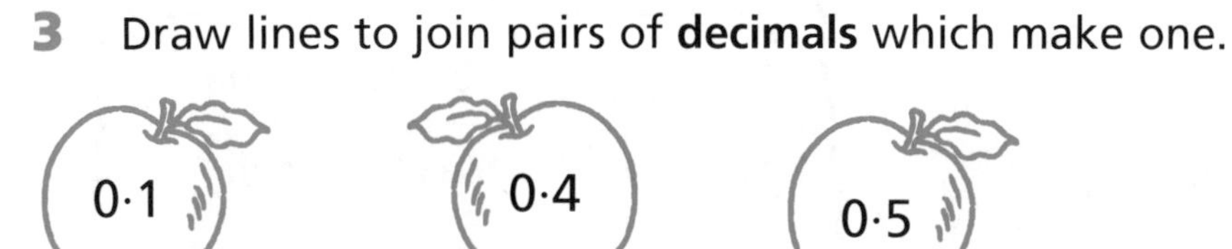

0·1 0·4 0·5 0·3 0·8

0·5 0·9 0·7 0·6 0·2

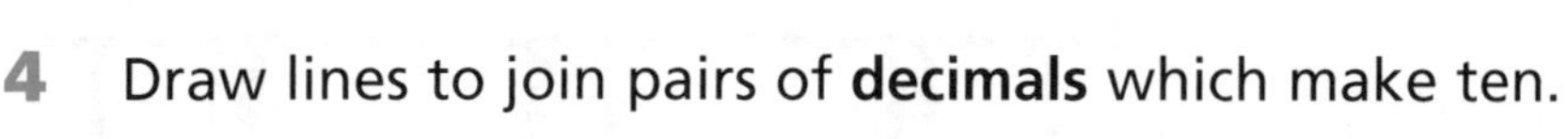

4 Draw lines to join pairs of **decimals** which make ten.

1·6 2·6 9·7 3·5 4·8 6·5

8·4 7·4 0·3 5·2

5 Find the answers to these calculations using near doubles to help you.

1·4 + 1·5 → double 1·5 = 3
3 − 0·1 = 2·9

1·9 + 2·0 → double ☐ = ☐
☐ − 0·1 = ☐

2·5 + 2·6 → double ☐ = ☐
☐ + 0·1 = ☐

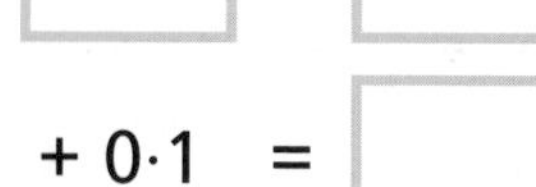

4·5 + 4·4 → double ☐ = ☐
☐ ☐ ☐ = ☐

Jim's cafe

OPENING TIMES

Sunday	10 a.m. – 4 p.m.
Monday	9 a.m. – 5 p.m.
Tuesday	10 a.m. – 5 p.m.
Wednesday	10 a.m. – 5 p.m.
Thursday	9 a.m. – 1 p.m.
Friday	10 a.m. – 6 p.m.
Saturday	9 a.m. – 7 p.m.

1 How many hours is the cafe open each day?

Sunday ________ hours

Monday ________ hours

Tuesday ________ hours

Wednesday ________ hours

Thursday ________ hours

Friday ________ hours

Saturday ________ hours

2 Show this information on the **bar-line graph** below.

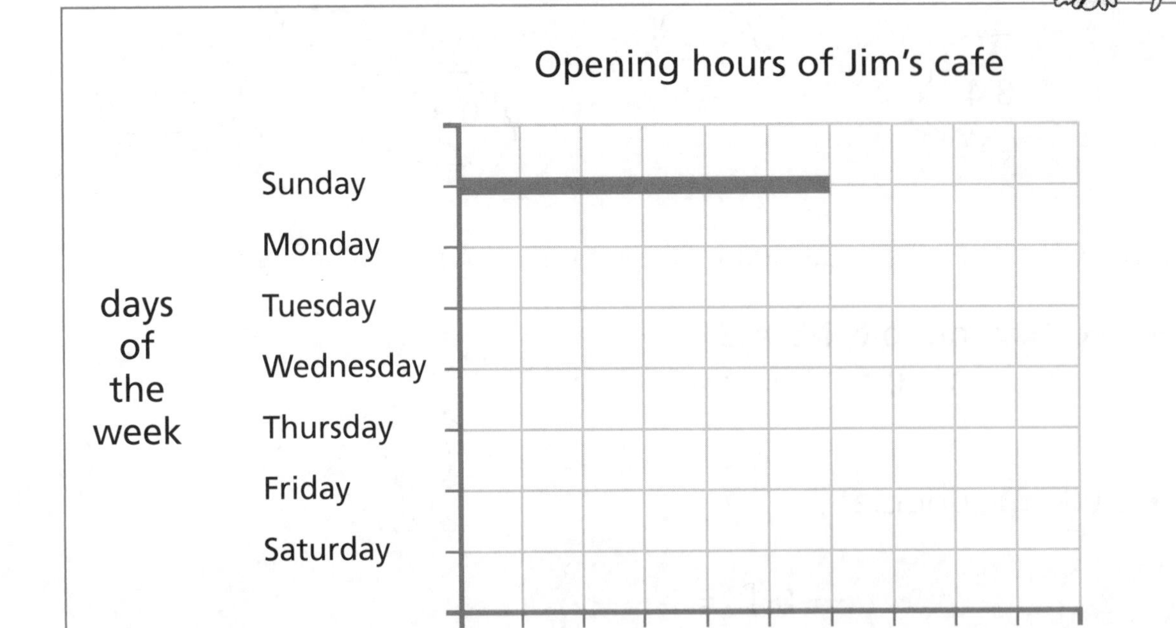

3 On which day is the cafe open longest? ________

4 On which day is the cafe open the least number of hours? ________

5 What is the difference between the longest and the shortest opening times in minutes? ________

Ink spots

All answers will be square units.
Area is the space inside a shape.

Work out the **area** that each ink spot covers. Each time, write the total number of squares.

If more than half a square is covered, then count it as one square. If less than half a square is covered, then do not count it.

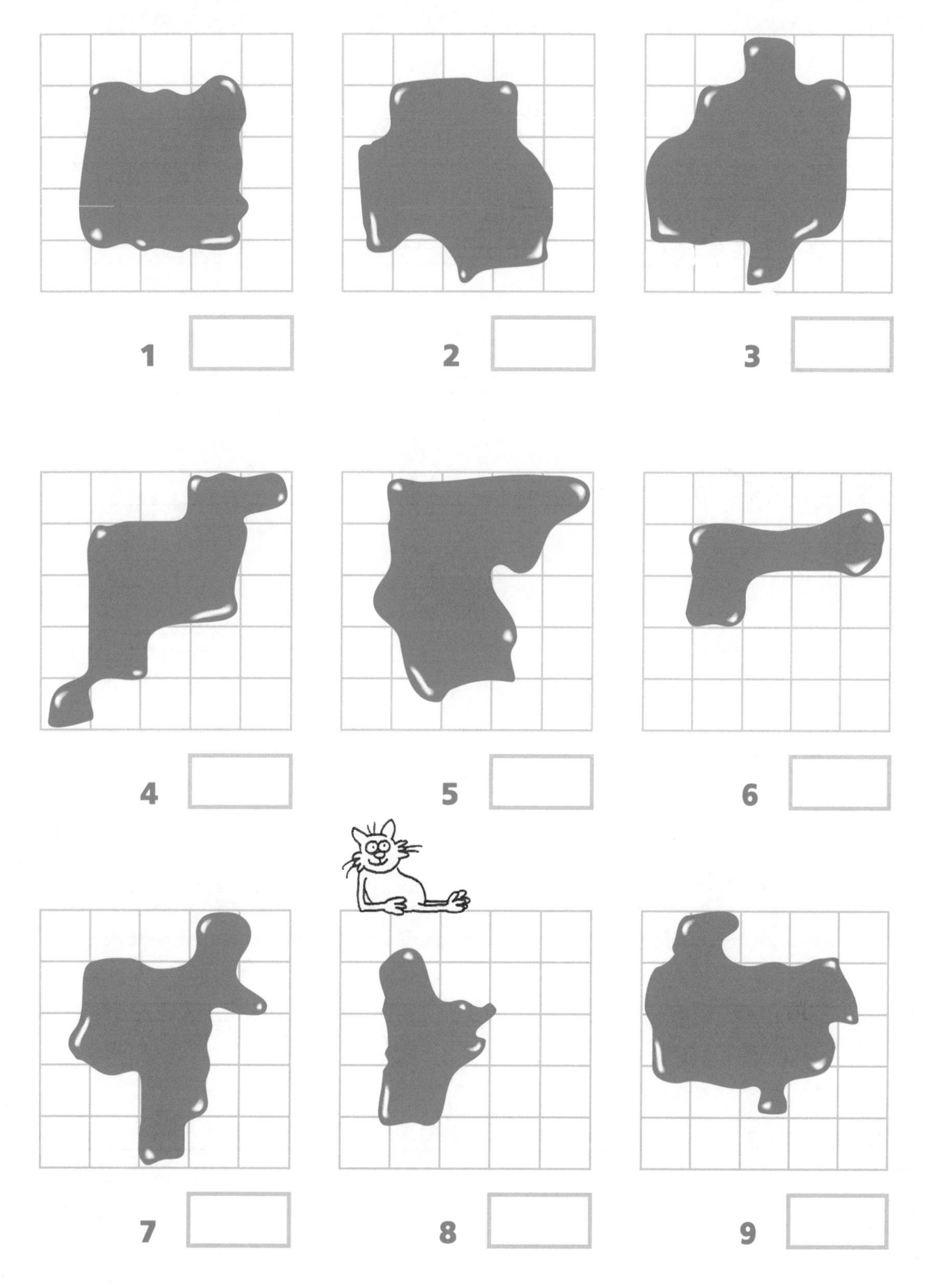

Number patterns

The first one has been done for you!

Look at each **number pattern**.

Find the relationship between the numbers.

Calculate what the tenth number in each series will be.

		RELATIONSHIP	TENTH NUMBER
1	1 3 5 7 9	add 2	19
2	30 28 26 24 22		
3	3 6 9 12 15		
4	50 45 40 35 30		
5	2 13 24 35 46		
6	–2 –3 –4 –5 –6		
7	8 17 26 35 44		
8	100 93 86 79 72		
9	10 8 6 4 2		

Sorting numbers

Look at these numbers.

1 Use this **decision tree** diagram to sort the numbers.

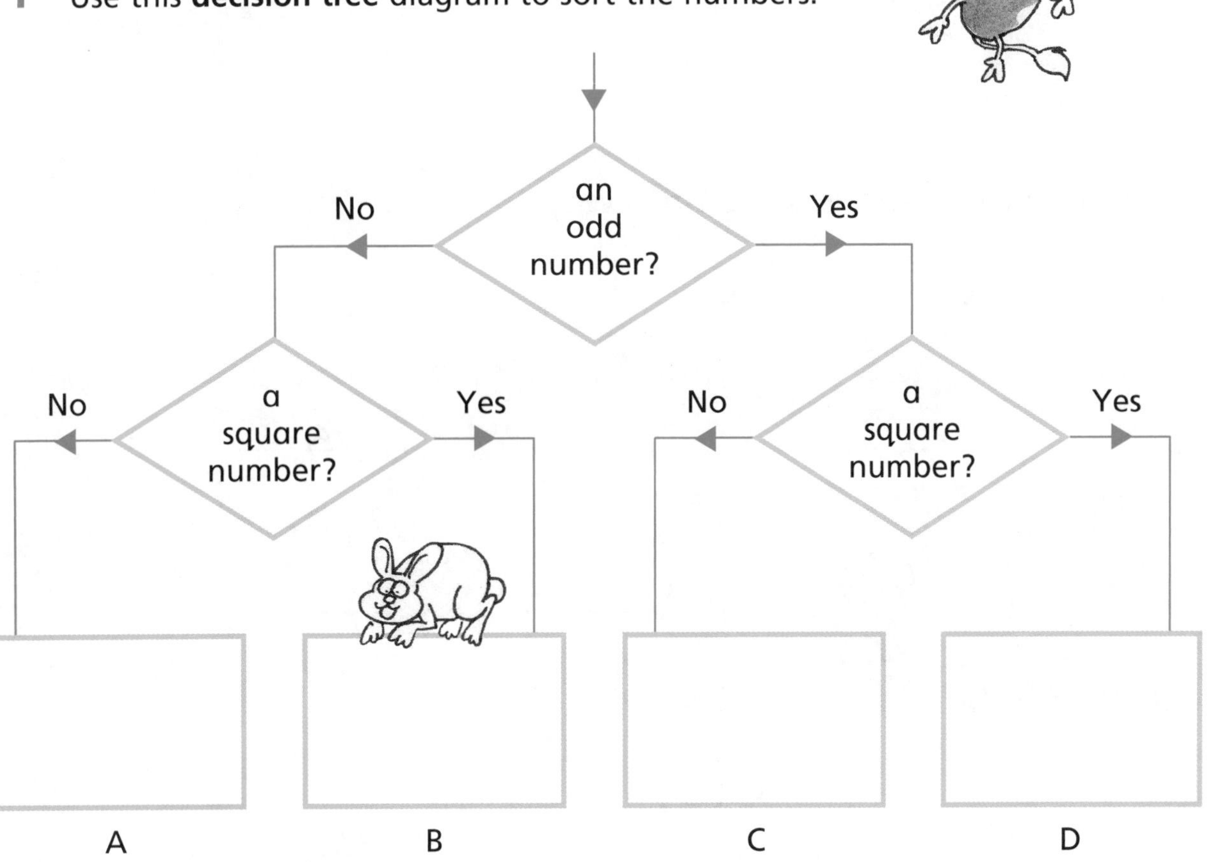

2 What two properties do the numbers in D share?

______________ and ______________

3 What two properties do the numbers in B share?

______________ and ______________

4 What difference is there between the numbers in A and B?

____

5 Why would 16 and 49 be in different places?

____

Hard times

You can find the answer to 243 × 4

like this:

200 × 4 = 800
40 × 4 = 160
3 × 4 = 12
972

or like this:

243
× 4
972
1 1

*When **multiplying** large numbers, break the numbers down into smaller units.*

Try these calculations using both ways.

1 126 × 5 → ☐ × 5 = ☐
☐ × 5 = ☐
☐ × 5 = ☐

126
× 5

2 344 × 6 → ☐ × 6 = ☐
☐ × 6 = ☐
☐ × 6 = ☐

344
× 6

3 478 × 4 → ☐ × 4 = ☐
☐ × 4 = ☐
☐ × 4 = ☐

478
× 4

Division

To find how many sixes there are in 642 use the **multiplication facts** you already know.

$$642 \div 6 \rightarrow \begin{array}{r} 100 \times 6 = 600 \\ 7 \times 6 = +42 \\ \hline 107 \times 6 = 642 \end{array}$$

You can see that $642 \div 6 = 107$.

Use this method to do these calculations.

1 $69 \div 3$ →

☐	× 3 =	30
☐	× 3 =	30
☐	× 3 =	+ 9
69 ÷ 3 = ☐	× 3 =	69

2 $48 \div 2$ →

☐	× 2 =	40
☐	× 2 =	+ 8
48 ÷ 2 = ☐	× 2 =	48

3 $165 \div 5$ →

☐	× 5 =	100
☐	× 5 =	50
☐	× 5 =	+15
165 ÷ 5 = ☐	× 5 =	165

4 $176 \div 4$ →

☐	× 4 =	80
☐	× 4 =	80
☐	× 4 =	+16
176 ÷ 4 = ☐	× 4 =	176

Choose your own multiplication facts to do these calculations.

5 $175 \div 5$

6 $372 \div 3$

Circling numbers

In each box, draw a circle around the numbers which have the correct **properties**.

The correct properties are shown in the top of each box.

1

Multiples of 5
190 73 85 136 124 90 15 205 201 360

2

Square numbers
18 25 100 144 91 169 77 1000 28 64

When a number is multiplied by itself it makes a ***square number.***

3

Prime numbers
21 53 81 97 14 11 17 39 49 29 2

4

Numbers which are multiples of 3 and multiples of 4
36 18 8 64 24 56 34 48 72 62 51

Multiples *of a number can be divided exactly by that number.*

5

Factors of 100

10 5 24 17 40 25 4 55 50 75 8

6

Odd numbers which are multiples of 7

21 23 70 49 140 77 35 41 28 62

Factors are numbers that exactly divide another number. 5 is a factor of 10.

7

Even numbers which are multiples of 3

10 19 5 78 17 58 55 35 36 42 6

8

Numbers which are not multiples of 9

81 19 90 99 290 89 55 18 99 63 101 270

Best bet

Which of each pair would give you the larger amount?
Colour the box.

1	$\frac{1}{2}$ of 15	a quarter of 36
2	$\frac{1}{5}$ of 20	0.9 of 20
3	25% of 100	a third of 90
4	a tenth of 40	$\frac{1}{4}$ of 24
5	0.5 of 80	$\frac{2}{3}$ of 42
6	75% of £200	0.6 of £200
7	$\frac{2}{5}$ of 60	two-thirds of 21
8	25% of 60	$\frac{1}{2}$ of 24
9	a quarter of 80	$\frac{4}{5}$ of 40
10	40% of £10	25% of £9

Starry sums

Work out the answer to each **calculation,** and write the answer in the star.

Draw a line to join stars of the same value.

How many of these calculations can you do in your head?
1
50% of 8
2
71 − 7
3
2 × 2 × 25
4
$\frac{1}{4}$ of 76
5
9 × 4
6
$5^2 - 6$
7
$\frac{1}{3}$ of 12
8
37 + 63
9
79 − 15
10
70 − 27
11
$\sqrt{9}$
12
(9 × 5) − 2
13
2.37 + 0.63
14
$\frac{1}{3}$ of 93
15
100 − 69
16
4^3

Colour stars with **prime number** answers orange.

Colour stars with **square number** answers green.

Snack time

Littleham School sells snacks at playtime.

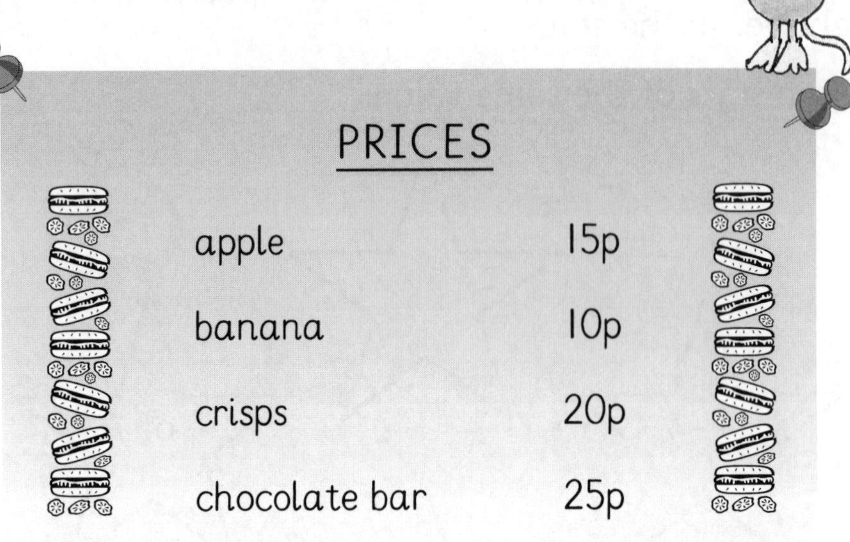

PRICES
apple 15p
banana 10p
crisps 20p
chocolate bar 25p

1 John buys an apple.

It costs ________________ . He has 50p.

He gets ________________ change.

2 Sean buys a chocolate bar. He has £1.00.

He gets ________________ change.

3 Harry buys an apple and a chocolate bar.

He spends ________________.

4 Alison has £1.00. She buys a chocolate bar and a packet of crisps.

How much change should she have? ________________

5 Which two items could Ali buy for exactly 35p?

____

6 Sean has two coins. He has just enough money to buy an apple.
What coins does he have?

__________ and __________

7 Helen wants to buy two bananas and a chocolate bar.
How much money does she need?

____

Joe and Sarah keep a tally of what food is sold.

FOOD	TALLY	TOTAL
Apples		19
Bananas		10
Crisps		11
Choc bars	~~||||~~ ~~||||~~ ~~||||~~ ~~||||~~	

8 Complete the **tally** chart.

9 Finish drawing the results on this **bar-line graph**.

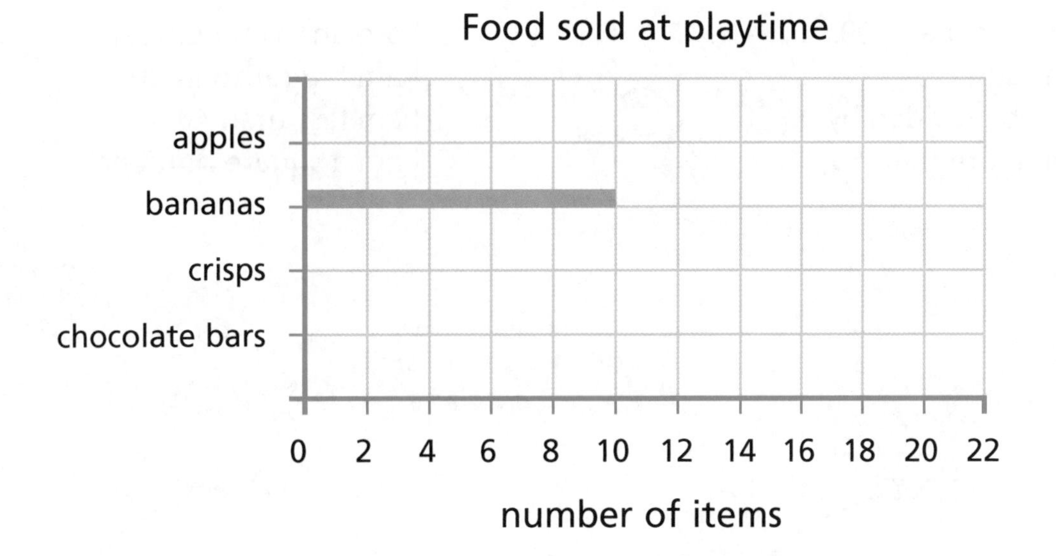

Joe and Sarah count the money at the end of playtime.
They calculate how much they have taken for each item.

10 Finish their table.

Apples	19	@	15p	=	
Bananas	10	@	10p	=	
Crisps	11	@	20p	=	
Choc bars	20	@	25p	=	

To multiply 15p by 19p, you could multiply by 20, then take off one lot of 15p.

11 How much money did they take altogether? ____________________

Guess my number

Read each clue carefully. Decide which number fits all the clues. Draw a circle around it.

1

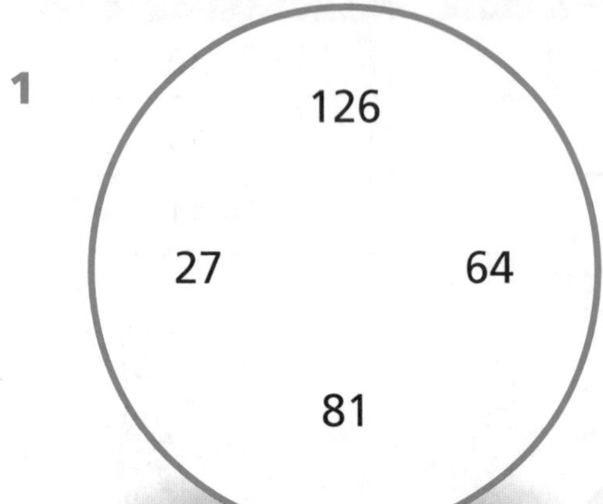

I am less than 100.
I am odd.
I can be divided by 9.
I am more than 50.

The clues give you the **properties** of the number.

2

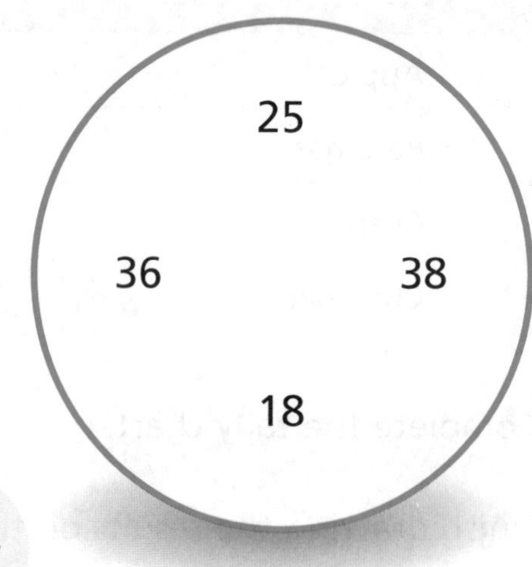

I am an even number.
I am bigger than 20.
I am less than 40.
I am a square number.

The answer is one of the numbers you are given.

3

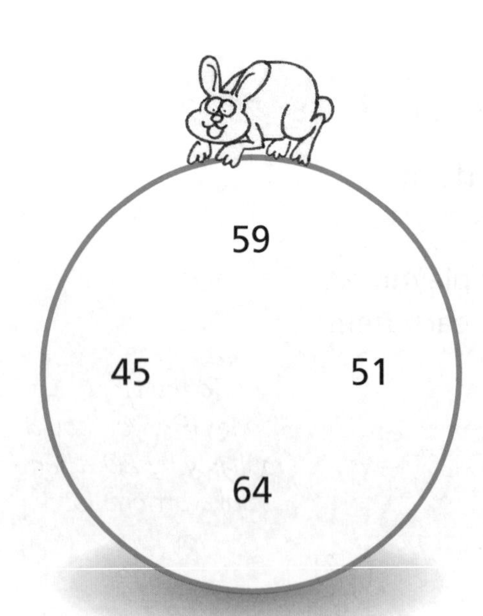

I am odd.
I am a prime number.
I am more than 50.

4

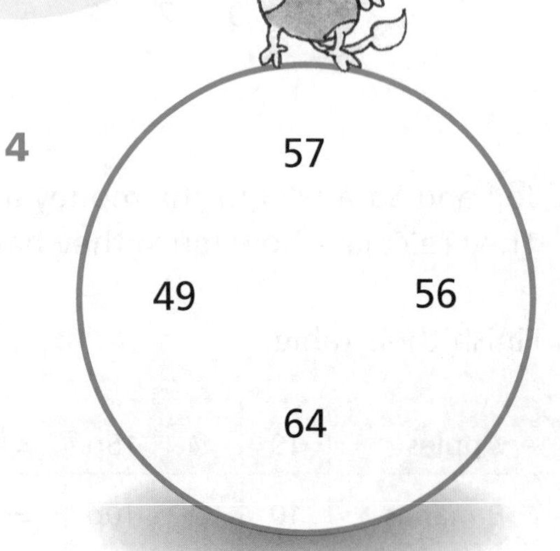

I am even.
I am divisible by 8.
I am divisible by 7.

5

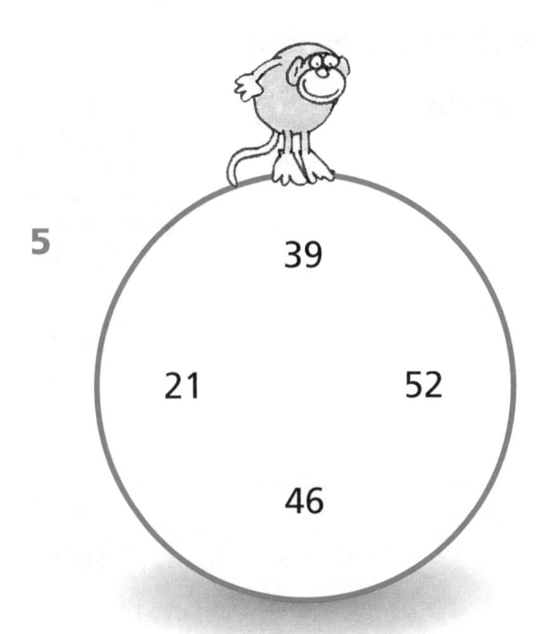

I am less than 7×7.

I am more than 5×5.

3 is one of my factors.

6

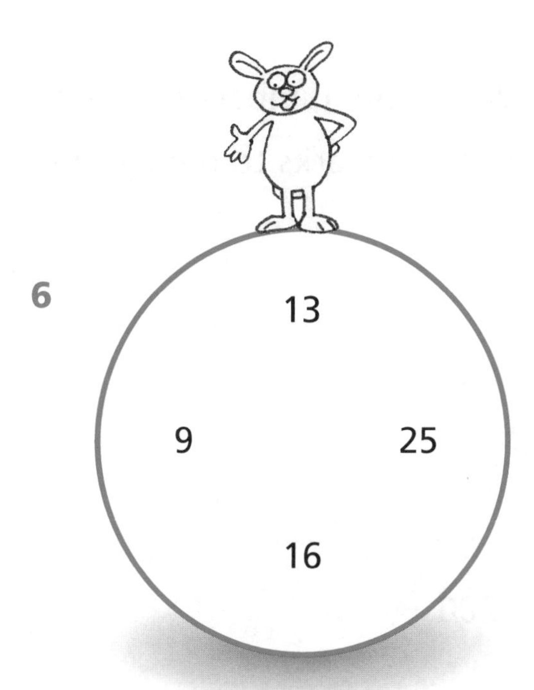

I am a square number.

I am an odd number.

I am not half of 50.

7

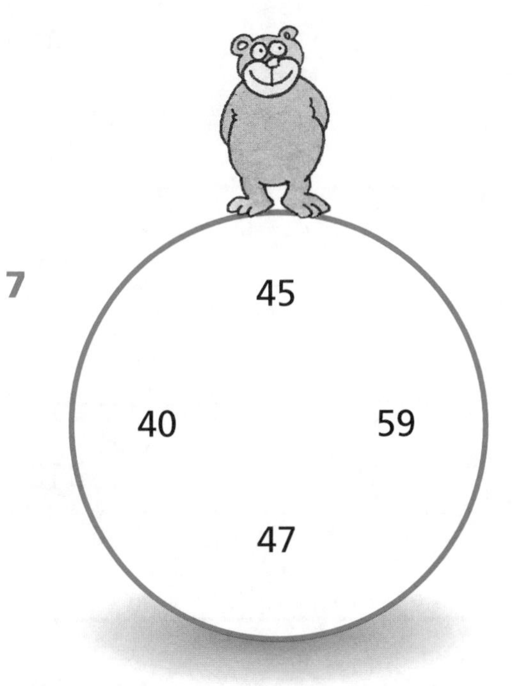

I am more than 6×7.

I am less than 9×6.

I am a prime number.

8

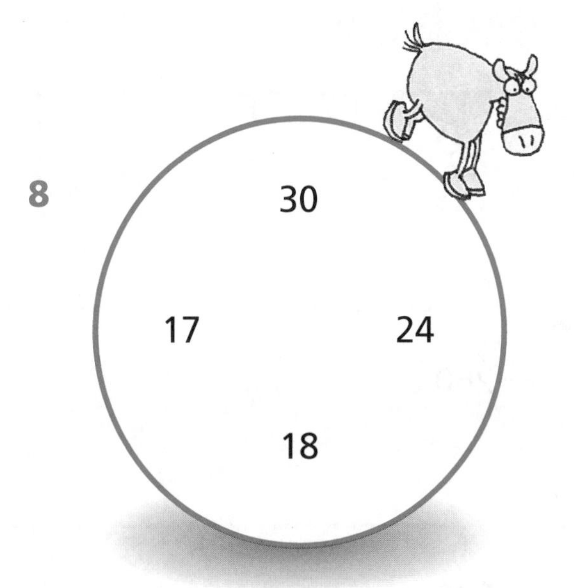

I am divisible by 2.

I am more than 3×9.

I am divisible by 3 and 10.

Number lines

Write the numbers that are missing in each **number line.**

Use the marks to help you work out the **scale**.

1 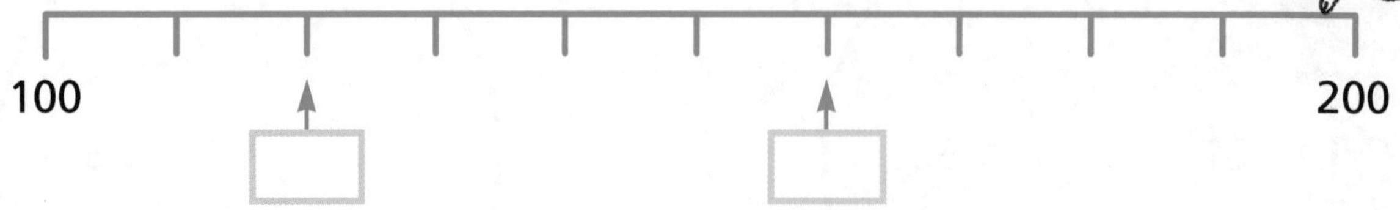 — 100 to 200

2 — 200 to 300

3 — –5 to 5

4 — 3 to 4

5 — 12 to 13

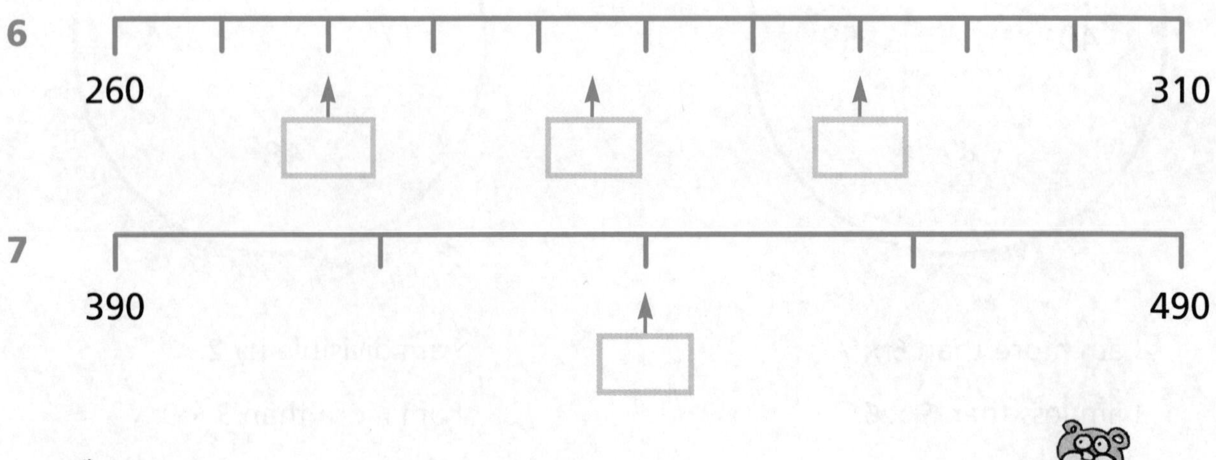

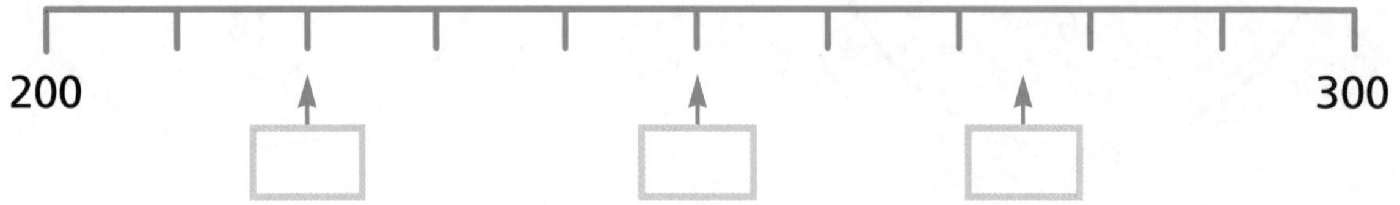

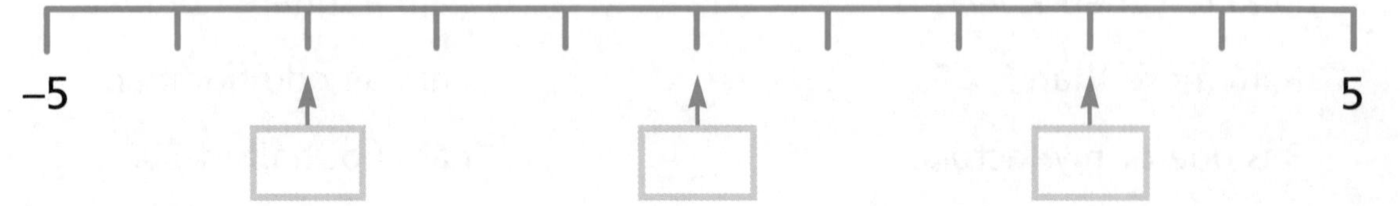

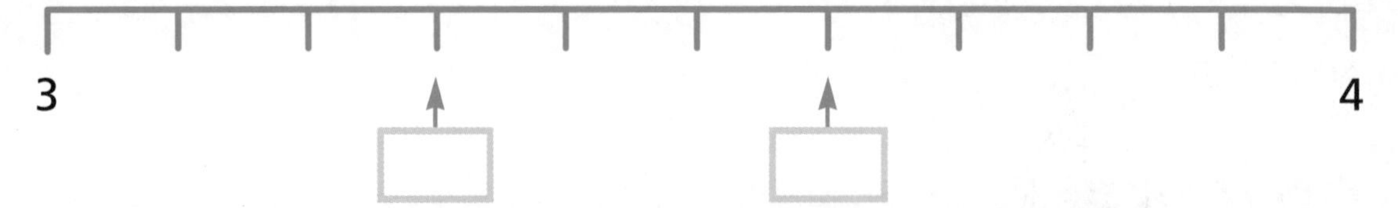

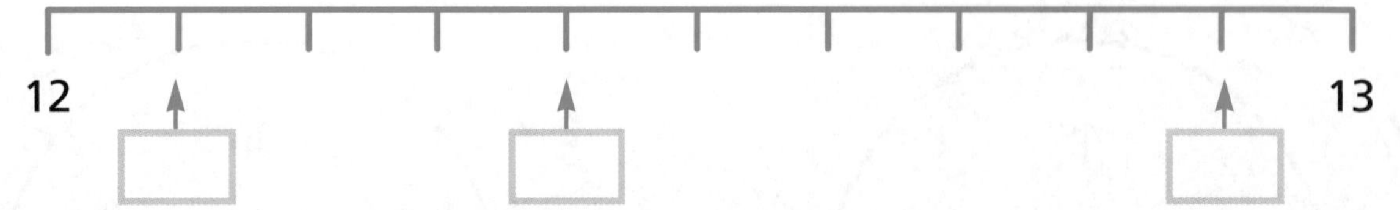

Countdown

Use the numbers given to make the **target**.

Use each number only once.

You do not need to use every number.

You can use any **operation**: +, −, × or ÷

Use brackets to show which operations should be done first.

The first one has been done for you.

	TARGET	NUMBERS	METHOD
1	154	100 9 7 6 3 1	100 + (9 × 6)
2	136	100 9 6 4 2 1	
3	91	100 7 5 3 2 1	
4	130	50 5 4 3 2 1	
5	400	100 10 8 5 4 1	
6	296	100 10 8 4 3 2	
7	172	100 10 9 8 6 2	
8	115	50 10 5 3 2 1	

Shapes and angles

Check your understanding of **angles.**

Here's a clue:
reflex angle is greater than 180° but less than 360°.

1 Draw a line to link the correct name to each drawing of an angle.

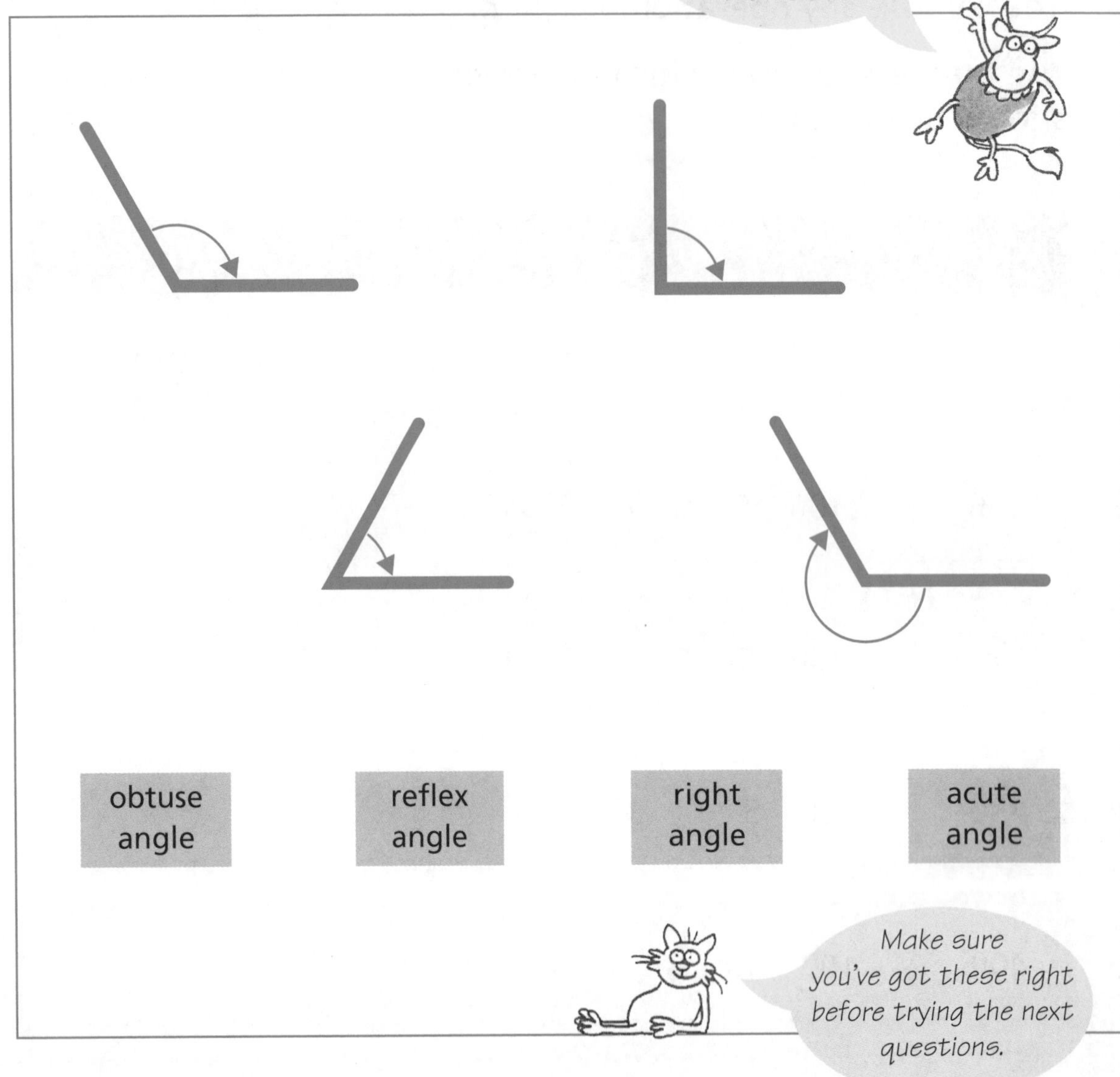
obtuse angle
reflex angle
right angle
acute angle
Make sure you've got these right before trying the next questions.

Look at the shapes drawn on the opposite page.

2 Which shapes have curved sides? ____________________

3 Which shapes contain an **acute angle?** ____________________

4 Which shapes have **parallel** sides? ____________________

5 Which shapes contain a **reflex angle?** ____________________

6 Which shapes contain an **obtuse angle?** ____________________

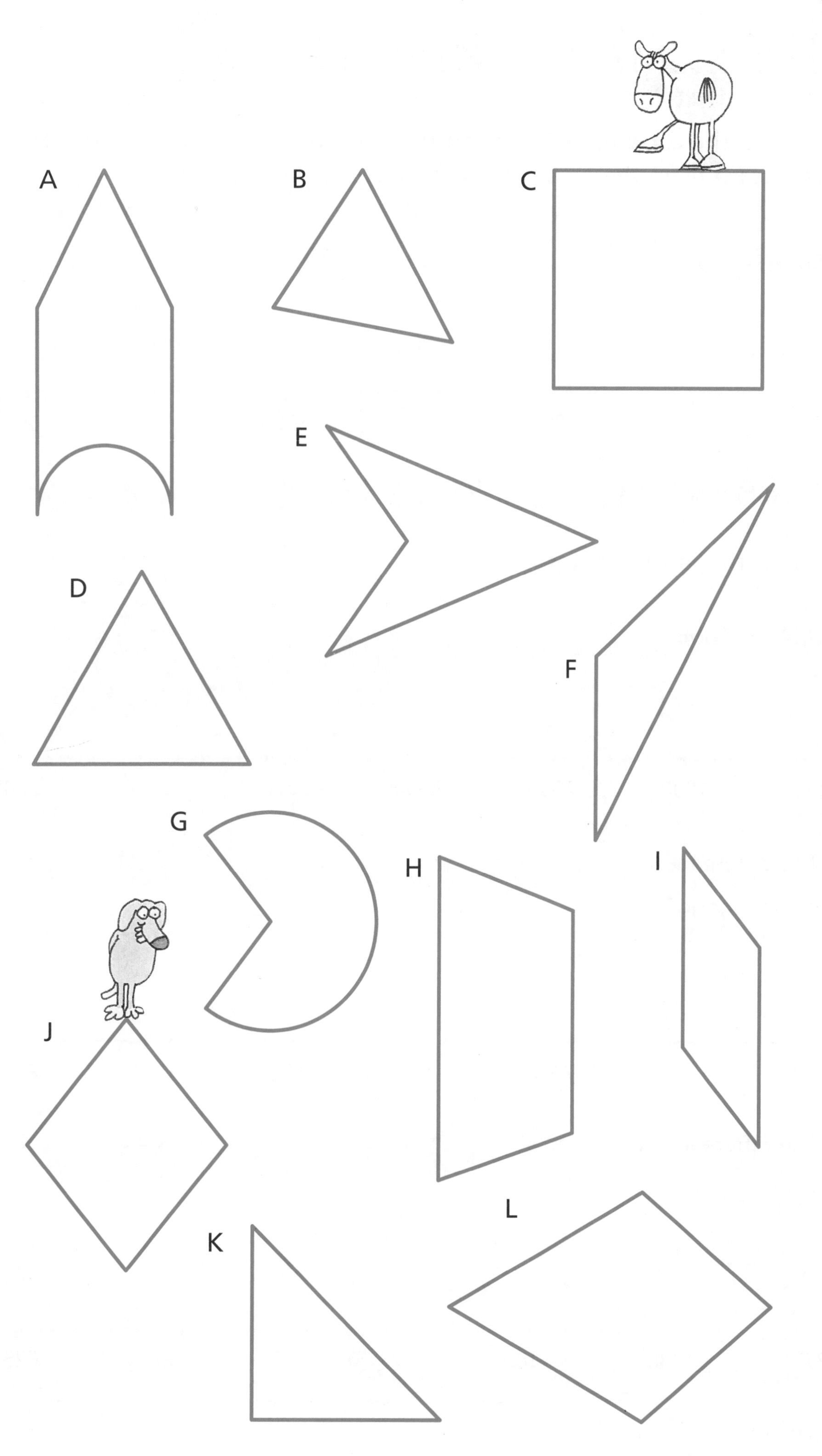
A
B
C
D
E
F
G
H
I
J
K
L

What's the difference?

To find the **difference** between two numbers it is often easiest to count up from the smallest to the largest number.

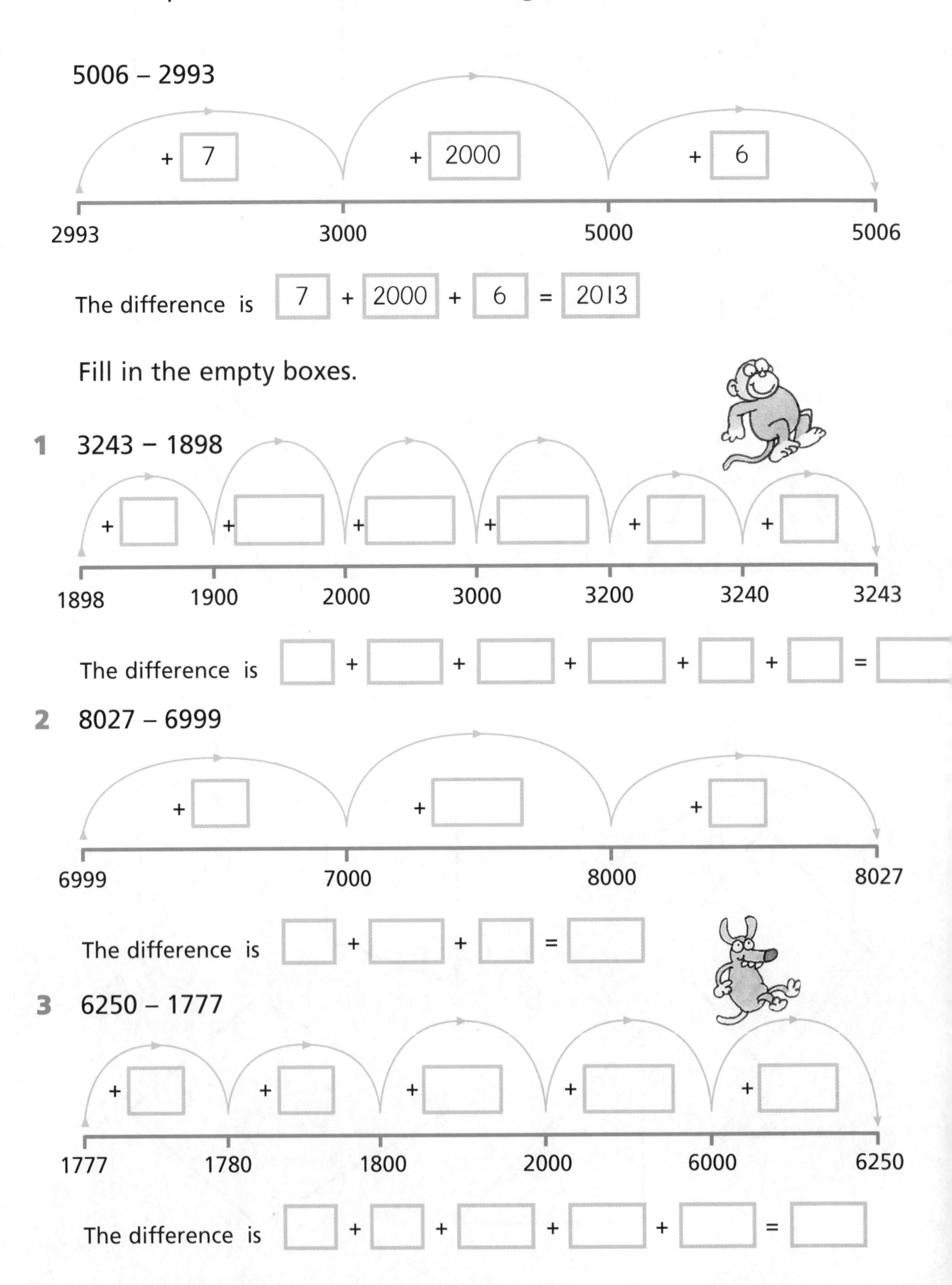

5006 – 2993

2993 → +7 → 3000 → +2000 → 5000 → +6 → 5006

The difference is 7 + 2000 + 6 = 2013

Fill in the empty boxes.

1 3243 – 1898

1898 → + ☐ → 1900 → + ☐ → 2000 → + ☐ → 3000 → + ☐ → 3200 → + ☐ → 3240 → + ☐ → 3243

The difference is ☐ + ☐ + ☐ + ☐ + ☐ + ☐ = ☐

2 8027 – 6999

6999 → + ☐ → 7000 → + ☐ → 8000 → + ☐ → 8027

The difference is ☐ + ☐ + ☐ = ☐

3 6250 – 1777

1777 → + ☐ → 1780 → + ☐ → 1800 → + ☐ → 2000 → + ☐ → 6000 → + ☐ → 6250

The difference is ☐ + ☐ + ☐ + ☐ + ☐ = ☐

Distance table

This table shows the distance between some cities, measured in kilometres.

	Cardiff	Glasgow	London	York
Cardiff		608	249	389
Glasgow	608		394	340
London	249	394		315
York	389	340	315	

1 How far is it from Cardiff to Glasgow? ________________

2 What is the distance from York to London? ________________

3 Write down the distance from London to Glasgow. ________________

4 How far is it from York to Cardiff? ________________

5 Mr Tomm drove from London to Cardiff.
He drove on to York.
How far did he travel altogether? ________________

6 Which of the three other cities is the nearest one to London?

____

7 Mrs Hill drove from Glasgow to London.
She then returned home to Glasgow.
How far did she travel altogether? ________________

8 What is the difference in distance between the journey from London to Glasgow, and the journey from Cardiff to York? ________________

9 Bob worked in all four cities.
He wanted to live in the city that would give him least travelling.
Which city was best for him to live in?

____

Decimal duos

Choose two numbers from the box.
Add them together.
If the answer is on the grid then write the sum in the square.

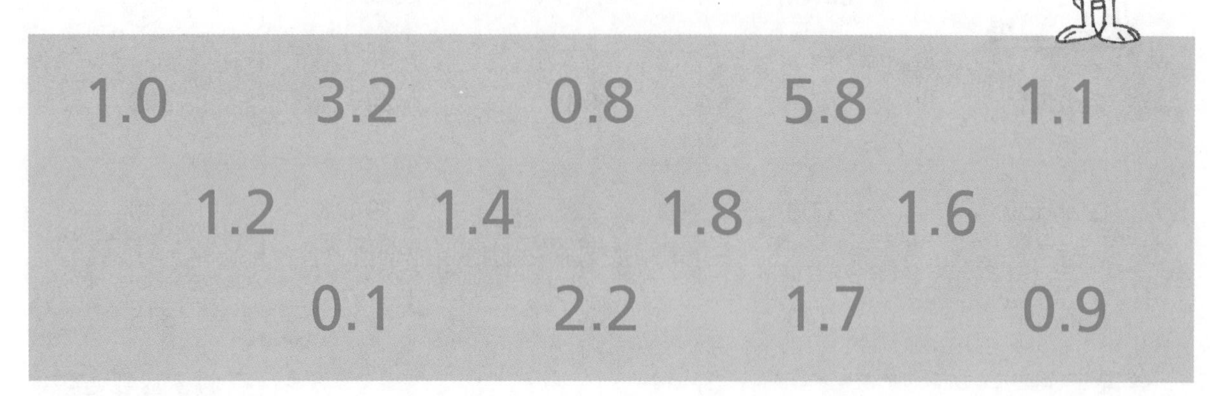

The first one has been done for you. Carry on until you have a sum in every square.

1.7 0.9 + 0.8	2.8	1.5	3.8
1.9	2.9	6.8	4.9
2.1	3.5	0.9	2.3
4.1	5.0	3.3	2.2

Answers and Hints

There may be more than one way to reach an answer. As long as your child reaches the right answer by calculating accurately (you will need to check their workings) you should mark the answer right. However, be careful to check that they have understood the method shown. In some instances more than one answer may be possible.

PAGE 5
1 974 2 174 3 971 4 714 5 794 6 197 7 197 8 497 9 147, 174, 417, 471, 714 or 741 (all these numbers can be divided by three since the sum of their digits is 12 which itself exactly divisible by three) 10 174 or 714 (number must be even to divide by two)

PAGE 6
1 Animal Stories: 10, Scary Stories: 18 2 4 3 56 4 20

PAGE 7
In the boxes: (top left) A; (top right) B; (bottom left) C, E; (bottom right) D

PAGES 8 & 9
1 (a) 10p, (b) 9°, (c) 47p, (d) 22°, (e) £32, (f) 13° 2 (a) 12p, (b) 8°, (c) 13p, (d) 6°, (e) £24, (f) 13° 3 (a) 3, 4, (b) 30, 15 4 (top group) 5, 9; (bottom group) 8°C, 15°C 5 (a) 59p, 16p, 37p, (b) 15, 143, 142

PAGE 10
There are other possibilities, but here is one example for each 20 $(2 + 3) \times 4$ 19 $(4 \times 5) - 1$ 18 $(4 + 2) \times 3$ 17 $3 \times (4 + 2) - 1$ 16 $4 \times (3 + 1)$ 15 $3 \times (4 + 1)$ 14 $(3 \times 4) + 2$ 13 $(3 \times 4) + 1$ 12 3×4

PAGE 11
1 each answer should have been the same as the number your child first thought of 2 100

PAGES 12 & 13
1 $\times 8$ 2 $\div 4$ 3 $+ 99$ 4 $- 21$

PAGE 14
1 5 2 1 3 −2 4 −6 5 3 6 −2

PAGE 15
1 230, The digits move **one** place to the **left** and a **zero** fills the units space 2 3700, The digits move **two** places to the left and **zeros** fill the **tens** and **units** spaces 3 6.3, The tens become **units**, the units become **tenths** and there is a **decimal point** between them 4 1.25, The hundreds become **units**, the tens become **tenths**, the units become **hundreths** 5 (first column) 1680, 3.74, 8900, 49800, .32; (second column) 5.7, 5020, 25750, 487.2

PAGES 16 & 17
1 totals (top to bottom): 3, 2, 6, 2, 6, 1, 3, 1, 3, 0, 1, 2 2 20 3 10 4 30 5 5 6 January, July and September 7 6 8 4 boys 9 February should be 2 not 1, May should be 6 not 7, July should be 3 not 2 10 5 11 October 12 $\frac{1}{5}$ 13 $\frac{2}{3}$

PAGE 18
1 in the boxes: (A) in, to, of; (B) me; (C) from, book; (D) then, page, pencil 2 D, because it has more than 3 letters and contains the letter 'e' 3 B, because it has no more than 3 letters and contains the letter 'e'

PAGE 19
1 multiples of 5: 5, 25, 50; overlap: 35, 70; multiples of 7: 7, 14, 42, 56; outside the circles: 11, 13, 17 2 Check your child has chosen multiples of 5, 9 and both (and some other numbers which are neither) and has put them in the right places on the diagram.

PAGE 20
1 $\frac{1}{4}$ 2 $\frac{1}{2}$ 3 $\frac{1}{4}$ 4 cola 5 12 6 6 7 18 8 50% 9 25%

PAGE 21
There should be nine fish coloured green: 4, 9, 16, 25, 36, 49, 64, 81 and 100.

PAGE 22
In both questions the three fractions add up to 1 – check that your child is aware of this, and can explain why this is so (because fractions are parts of a whole). 1 check your child has coloured each flag like this: 2 boxes red, 1 box green, 3 boxes blue 2 check your child has coloured each flag like this: 3 boxes red, 4 boxes yellow, 5 boxes blue

PAGE 23
Check your child's estimate against these actual lengths: A: 2.5 cm ($2\frac{1}{2}$ cm); B: 15.5 cm ($15\frac{1}{2}$ cm); C: 7 cm; D: 11.5 cm ($11\frac{1}{2}$ cm); E: 13.5 cm ($13\frac{1}{2}$ cm); F: 4 cm. Make sure they have calculated the correct difference between each estimate and the actual length (if there is a difference!). Measuring the wiggly lines with string is quite tricky, so be generous when judging your child's answer. Your child will need to lay the string along the line, mark the end of the line on the string with pencil and then measure the length they have marked on the string with a ruler.

PAGES 24 & 25
1 number of beads (left to right): 3, 6, 2, 9 2 1, 0, 5, 6 3 5, 2, 3, 1 4 8, 0, 2, 6 5 4, 2, 1, 9 6 2, 3, 8, 0 7 1105 (beads drawn: 1, 1, 0, 5) 8 144 (0, 1, 4, 4) 9 1032 (1, 0, 3, 2) 10 (1221) 1, 2, 2, 1

PAGE 26
1 (first column) 42, 6, 7, 42; (second column) 56, 8, 8, 56; (third column) 48, 6, 8, 48 2 (first column) 54, $9 \times 6 = 54$, $54 \div 6 = 9$, $54 \div 9 = 6$; (second column) 63, $9 \times 7 = 63$, $63 \div 7 = 9$, $63 \div 9 = 7$; (third column) 72, $9 \times 8 = 72$, $72 \div 8 = 9$, $72 \div 9 = 8$ 3 multiples of 6: 6, 12, 18, 24, 30, 36, 42, 48, 54, 60, 66, 72, 78, 84, 90, 96; multiples of 7: 7, 14, 21, 28, 35, 42, 49, 56, 63, 70, 77, 84, 91, 98; multiples of 8: 8, 16, 24, 32, 40, 48, 56, 64, 72, 80, 88, 96

PAGE 27
1 4 2 12 3 6 4 2 5 24 6 8 7 21–30 8 6 9 4

PAGES 28 & 29
1 prime numbers under 100 are: 2, 3, 5, 7, 11, 13, 17, 19, 23, 29, 31, 37, 41, 43, 47, 53, 59, 61, 67, 71, 73, 79, 83, 89, 91 and 97. 2 this is true; here is one example for each (there are other possibilities): $12 = 5 + 7$, $18 = 7 + 11$, $24 = 11 + 13$, $30 = 13 + 17$, $36 = 5 + 31$, $42 = 11 + 31$, $50 = 7 + 43$ 3 again, this is true; here are some possible solutions: $13 = 3 + 3 + 7$, $23 = 5 + 7 + 11$, $29 = 5 + 11 + 13$, $31 = 3 + 11 + 17$, $53 = 11 + 19 + 23$

PAGE 30
Encourage your child to write fractions in the lowest possible value. If they have answered these questions by counting the shaded squares and writing that number over the total of all the squares, then they are not cancelling fractions down to their lowest denominator. You will need to show how to cancel down, e.g. $\frac{2}{4} = \frac{1}{2}$ when both the top and bottom numbers of the first fraction are divided by 2. 1 $\frac{1}{3}$ 2 $\frac{2}{3}$ 3 $\frac{1}{4}$ 4 $\frac{2}{3}$ 5 $\frac{1}{2}$ 6 $\frac{1}{2}$ 7 $\frac{1}{3}$ 8 number of coloured segments: (a) 2, (b) 2, (c) 6, (d) 1, (e) 8, (f) 5, (g) 2

PAGES 32 & 33
1 impossible: B, D; even: C; certain: G; check your child's answers to E and F to see that they are appropriate for them 2 unlikely – your child should identify the element of chance in rolling a dice 3 Spinner A, because it has two 2s and B only has one. 4 Spinner B, because it has four numbers of 3 or more, and A has only two.

PAGES 34 & 35

1 12 2 netball 3 football and swimming 4 Martin 5 6 6 2 7 Ian played netball and football. 8 Luke and Amy 9 Check that the circles are labelled (swimming, football and netball) and that the names are correctly placed: (just swimming) Shasta, Ellie; (just football) John, Lauren, Michael; (just netball) Isabel, Rosie, Luke, Andy; (swimming and football) Paul, Sean; (swimming and netball) Hannah; (football and netball) Josie; (all three sports) Alice

PAGE 36

1 numbers on the shirts (left to right) 50000, 60464, 61001, 89678, 99999, 156724, 400026, 500000 2 sixty thousand, four hundred and sixty four 3 four hundred thousand and twenty six 4 (left to right) –9, –7, –4, –3, –1, 0, 2, 3, 6, 8

PAGE 37

Check that your child's two answers are the same for each sum, and talk to them about which method they found easiest. 1 612 2 922 3 957

PAGE 38

1 totals in each interval (top to bottom): 2, 4, 6, 9, 3; check that the tally marks and totals match 2 5 3 6 4 3 5 16–20 6 1 and 5 7 2 8 16–20 9 11 10 23 (25 – 2)

PAGE 39

Stones with correct answers: $\sqrt{49}$ [= 7], (5 × 5) + 4 [= 29], (32 ÷ 4) – 1 [= 7], (8 × 5) + 1 [= 41], $\sqrt{169}$ [= 13], 100 – 3 [= 97], $\sqrt{25}$ [= 5], (3 × 4) – 1 [= 11], (100 ÷ 10) + 9 [= 19], (6 × 2) + 5 [= 17], (90 ÷ 9) + 3 [= 13].

PAGES 40 & 41

1 numbers on the shorts (left to right): 0.09, 0.13, 0.21, 0.72, 1.08, 1.23 2 (b) 1.2, 1; (c) 2.4, 2; (d) 2.9, 3; (e) 3.5, 4 (always round up if the decimal number is 5 or above); (f) 3.8, 4 3 0.1 + 0.9, 0.4 + 0.6, 0.5 + 0.5, 0.3 + 0.7, 0.8 + 0.2 4 1.6 + 8.4, 2.6 + 7.4, 9.7 + 0.3, 3.5 + 6.5, 4.8 + 5.2 5 Using near doubles is a short cut to finding the answer – the child uses what they know already to solve the problem: double 2.0 = 4.0, 4 – 0.1 = 3.9; double 2.5 = 5.0, 5.0 + 0.1 = 5.1; double 4.5 = 9.0, 9.0 – 0.1 = 8.9 (or double 4.4 = 8.8, 8.8 + 0.1 = 8.9)

PAGE 42

1 opening hours (top to bottom): 6, 8, 7, 7, 4, 8, 10
2 The bars on the graph should match the information from Question 1. 3 Saturday 4 Thursday 5 360

PAGE 43

1 9 2 11 3 13 4 10 5 11 6 5 7 8 8 4 9 10

PAGE 44

2 subtract 2, 12 3 add 3, 30 4 subtract 5, 5 5 add 11, 101 6 subtract 1, –11 7 add 9, 89 8 subtract 7, 37 9 subtract 2, –8

PAGE 45

1 in the boxes: (A) 42, 86; (B) 4, 100; (C) 35, 93; (D) 25, 81
2 odd numbers and square numbers 3 even numbers and square numbers 4 B numbers are square 5 both are square numbers, but 49 is odd and 16 is not

PAGE 46

Check that your child's two answers are the same for each calculation, and talk to them about which method they found easiest. 1 630 2 2064 3 1912

PAGE 47

1 69 ÷ 3 = 23 (10 + 10 + 3) 2 48 ÷ 2 = 24 (20 + 4)
3 165 ÷ 5 = 33 (20 + 10 + 3) 4 176 ÷ 4 = 44 (20 + 20 + 4)
5 175 ÷ 5 = 35 (20 + 10 + 5)
6 372 ÷ 3 = 124 (100 + 10 + 10 + 4)

PAGES 48 & 49

1 15, 85, 90, 190, 205, 360 2 25, 64, 100, 144, 169 3 2, 11, 17, 29, 53, 97 4 24, 36, 48, 72 5 4, 5, 10, 25, 50 6 21, 35, 49, 77 7 6, 36, 42, 78 8 19, 55, 89, 101, 290

PAGE 50

1 your child should have coloured the right-hand box ($\frac{1}{2}$ of 15 = 7.5, $\frac{1}{4}$ of 36 = 9) 2 right-hand box ($\frac{1}{5}$ of 20 = 4, 0.9 of 20 = 18) 3 right-hand box (25% of 100 = 25, $\frac{1}{3}$ of 90 = 30) 4 left-hand box ($\frac{1}{10}$ of 40 = 4, 1/4 of 24 = 6)
5 right-hand box (0.5 of 80 = 40, $\frac{2}{3}$ of 42 = 28)
6 left-hand box (75% of £200 = £150, 0.6 of £200 = £120)
7 left-hand box ($\frac{2}{5}$ of 60 = 24, $\frac{2}{3}$ of 21 = 14) 8 left-hand box (25% of 60 = 15, $\frac{1}{2}$ of 24 = 12) 9 right-hand box ($\frac{1}{4}$ of 80 = 20, $\frac{4}{5}$ of 40 = 32) 10 left-hand box (40% of £10 = £4, 25% of £9 = £2.25)

PAGE 51

1 4 2 64 3 100 4 19 5 36 6 19 7 4 8 100 9 64 10 43 11 3 12 43 13 3 14 31 15 31 16 64 Joined up stars: 1 & 7, 2 & 16, 3 & 8, 4 & 6, 9 & 16, 10 & 12, 11 & 13, 14 & 15. Orange stars: 4, 6, 10, 11, 12, 13, 14, 15. Green stars: 1, 2, 3, 5, 7, 8, 9, 16.

PAGES 52 & 53

1 15p, 5p 2 75p 3 40p 4 55p 5 apple and crisps, or banana and chocolate bar 6 10p and 5p 7 35p 8 check the tally marks match the total; the chocolate bar total is 20 9 check the graph matches the totals 10 (top to bottom) £2.85, £1, £2.20, £5 11 £11.05

PAGE 54

1 81 2 36 3 59 4 56 5 39 6 9 7 47 8 30

PAGE 56

1 120, 160 2 220, 250, 275 3 –3, 0, 3 4 3.3, 3.6 5 12.1, 12.4, 12.9 6 270, 282.5, 295 7 440

PAGE 57

There are other possibilities, but here is an example for each 2 136 = 100 + (9 × 4) 3 91 = 100 – (7 + 2)
4 130 = (50 × 3) – (5 × 4) 5 400 = 100 × 4
6 296 = (100 × 3) – 4 7 172 = 100 + (9 × 8)
8 115 = (50 × 2) + 10 + 5

PAGES 58 & 59

1 connecting lines: (top left) obtuse angle [between 90° and 180°]; (bottom left) acute angle [less than 90°]; (top right) right angle [90°]; (bottom right) reflex angle [over 180°] 2 A, G 3 A, B, D, E, F, H, I, J, K, L 4 A, C, H, I, J 5 E, G 6 A, F, H, I, J, L

PAGE 60

1 2, 100, 1000, 200, 40, 3 (total = 1345) 2 1, 1000, 27 (total = 1028) 3 3, 20, 200, 4000, 250 (total = 4473)

PAGE 61

1 608 km 2 315 km 3 394 km 4 389 km 5 638 km 6 Cardiff 7 788 km 8 5 km 9 London (the sum of the distances between London and the other cities is the smallest)

PAGE 62

There are quite a few possibilities, but here is one example for each (left to right): (first row) 1.8 + 1.0, 1.4 + 0.1, 2.2 + 1.6; (second row) 1.0 + 0.9, 1.8 + 1.1, 5.8 + 1.0, 3.2 + 1.7; (third row) 1.2 + 0.9, 1.7 + 1.8, 0.8 + 0.1, 1.2 + 1.1; (fourth row) 3.2 + 0.9, 3.2 + 1.8, 3.2 + 0.1, 1.2 + 1.0